Fascinating Fastener Facts
including
The Book of Rivet Revelations
and a
Smattering of Nonsense

Dave Galey

Winlock Galey
Publisher of Bus Conversion Books
Sun City, California

Fascinating Fastener Facts

including
The Book of Rivet Revelations
and a
Smattering of nonsense

Dave Galey

Published by : **Winlock Galey**
26135 Murrieta Road
Sun City, CA 92585

Library of Congress Catalog Number: 97-62174

ISBN No: 1-890461-00-8

The photograph on the cover reveals the following Busnuts beginning with Lois Thornhill, the lady in the straw hat, George Thornhill, Roberta Galey, the Author, Ruby Lee, Bill Young, Phyllis Howell, Fred Mengarelli, and Bob Howell

Other Books by Dave Galey

The Bus Converter's Bible

The Joys of Busing

The Gospel of Gauges
According to Galey

Classy Cabinets
for
Converted Coaches

This book is dedicated to all those

Bus Nuts

who smash their thumb, break drills,
and get glue on their fingers
so they can't let go of anything;

who with dedication, frustration

and

pride

create their own luxury motorhome

Table of Contents

Warning-Disclaimer

This book is designed to provide information only on the subject matter covered. It is sold with the understanding that the publisher and author are not engaged in rendering legal, accounting, engineering, or other professional services. If legal or other expert assistance is required, the services of a competent professional should be sought.

It is not the purpose of this manual to reprint all the information otherwise available to the author and/or publisher, but to complement, amplify and supplement other texts. You are urged to read all the available material, learn as much as possible about bus conversion and to tailor the information to your individual needs.

Every effort has been made to make this manual as complete and as accurate as possible. However, there may be mistakes both typographical and in content. Therefore, this text should be used only as a general guide and not as the ultimate source of bus conversion. Furthermore, this manual contains information on bus conversion only up to the printing date.

The purpose of this manual is to educate and entertain. The author and *WINLOCK GALEY* shall have neither liability nor responsibility to any person or entity with respect to any loss or damage caused, or alleged to be caused, directly or indirectly by the information contained in this book.

If you do not wish to be bound by the above, you may return this book to the publisher for a full refund

Preface

By way of a preface the reader is entitled to understand a bit about the author. To say that I am a religious person might be an understatement. I began my education by attending a Catholic boy's school where I was systematically whipped into shape and developed a huge guilt complex. I discovered almost anything I enjoyed was sinful. So, I sought Judaism. After failing to understand the Torah and not wanting to close up on Saturday, I decided to climb the mountain to enlightenment seeking the serenity of Buddha. Mohammed was next followed by a UFO cult. Unwilling to believe why any race more intelligent than our own would want to socialize with us, my quest for the truth continued.

About twenty years before the millennium, I discovered buses. I should say **B**uses (note the capitalization). Ahhh . . . Glorious Buses. I became a devoted follower. I was consumed and hence, consumed anything I could find about Buses. I hung on every word uttered by the great gurus. And, it came to pass I was inspired. I began to write, and write, and write some more. My hands were possessed. I had no control and in time my tome was complete: The Bible was done. As it turned out, I was unwittingly the instrument of the Great White Bus which stops at the Pearly Gates. I unknowingly became anointed as the Prophet: the Prophet of the Church of Busology. I didn't ask for this awesome responsibility. It was simply thrust upon me. It has thus become my mission in life. Finally, after years of aimless wandering, my life has meaning. After the Bible, was the Joys, then the Gospel and now we have the book of Revelations, rivets, that is.

For those of you reading this, who are offended by my religious analogies, I apologize. Keep in mind, each of us must seek Paradise in our own way. For those of you who think I am being pretentious as the self declared Prophet of Busology, all I can say to you is, thbtts!!. Even Pogo was belittled when he first declared, "We have met the enemy, and it is us." This book was inspired by the overwhelming success of the Gospel . . . plus the fact that Don Whitehall e-mailed me one day and said, "Why don't you write a gospel on fasteners?" Not wanting to tread in my own footsteps I felt it may be a mild form of plagiarism to write another gospel. After all, I did copyright the Gospel so being a clever sort I put my brain into the Prophet mode and wah-lah, the Revelations emerged. I must say that writing a book about fasteners might tend to become a little boring so I felt it is important to inject a little nonsense from time to time.

What follows will be mostly my own opinion, and occasional peek at a reference manual and my own experiences.

Dave Galey

Fall 1997

Introduction

F astening is a broad topic. It can involve a variety of materials and a variety of techniques. For the most part we will discuss those types of fasteners primarily associated with joining bus parts. Welding, although is not specifically a fastener, is a method of joining and will also be included. Furthermore, adhesive bonding may be considered a continuous fastener in that it is much like welding.

The list following is composed of items classified as fasteners: Adhesives, Bolts, Brads, Brackets, Clips, Couplings, Glue, Hooks, Hasps, Hangars, Hinges, Latches, Nuts, Nails, Rivets, Screws, Snaps, Unions, Weld. Some items in the list will be emphasized more than others. For example, nails are seldom appropriate when joining bus parts, so they will be discarded from our text. The principle emphasis will be directed toward bolts and nuts, screws, welding, riveting, and adhesive bonding.

Skin panels have, in recent years, been glued, or adhesive bonded to the bus framework. Aircraft parts have been glued, or *metalbonded*, for nearly 40 years. It is only recently manufacturers have developed a product which may be safely used with minimally sophisticated equipment. For example, *metalbonding* in aircraft manufacture had to be handled with white gloves in a pressurized *clean* room, wrapped in a temperature resistant blanket, then have a vacuum drawn and baked in an autoclave (a pressurized oven). This is not a process which lends itself to the self-conversion specialist under a shade tree in the back yard.

Other items to be discarded from this book will be Brads, Brackets, Clips, Couplings, Glue, Hooks, Hasps, Hangars, Hinges, Latches, Snaps, and Unions. This leaves us with Adhesives, Bolts, Nuts, Rivets, Screws, and Welds. We will further breakdown these categories.

Structures 101 for Dummies

Iapologize for the title of this chapter since anyone reading this book is certainly no dummy. The purpose here is to provide a brief course in the use of fasteners and how they are loaded. Many of the examples illustrated are bolts but the loading would be the same be they rivets, screws, welds or glue.

There are several fundamental ways a bolt may be loaded. The first and simplest is pure tension. This is nothing more than loading the fastener in a way which attempts to pull it apart it length-wise. The drawing to the right shows a bolt being loaded in tension.

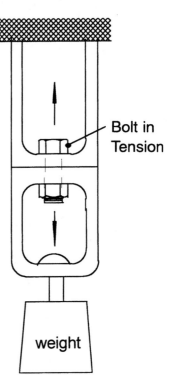

Bolt in Tension

weight

Tensile strength of a material has several significant values.

The ultimate strength is that value at which the material will fracture, rupture, come apart, or just plain break. The yield strength is that value where the material begins to deform under load and will stay *bent out of shape*, so to speak. From zero load up the yield point is the elastic range of the material and we often call the yield point the elastic limit. Any loading up to that elastic limit will allow the material to change shape but return to it's original shape after the load is removed.

As an example, common SAE 1020 hot rolled steel has an ultimate tensile strength of 63,000 pounds per square inch (psi). In other words, a 1 inch square bar would pull apart with a load of 63,000 pounds. It's yield strength, however is only 35, 000 psi. That is, if you load it to 40,000 pounds, it will stretch but not break. But also, it will not return to it's original length. . . it will be longer. If you had loaded it to only 33,000 pounds, it would stretch, but when the load was removed it would come back to it's original shape and dimensions. The values given in the tables to follow include a safety factor of 2

The next simplest form of fastener loading is shear. Shear is just like it sounds. The load tries to cut through the bolt just like a pair of scissors. In addition, shear may come in several flavors; single shear, double shear and multiple shear.

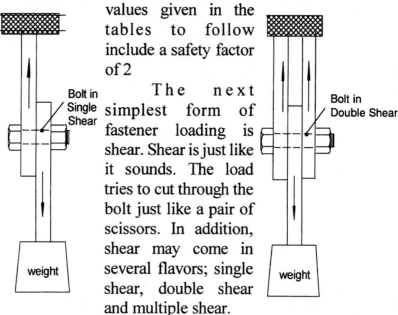

This isn't near as complex as it sounds. Single shear simply means the bolt is trying to be cut (or shorn)

through a single plane. As shown in these illustrations, the picture in the right shows the bolt resisting being shorn in two planes, hence we call this double shear. Interestingly, double shear is twice as strong as single shear. That is the bolt can resist twice the weight as it could in the picture on the left.

This concept may be expanded within limits. For example, a piano hinge may be considered a fitting which loads the pin (bolt) in multiple shear. Another form of multiple shear would be a finger joint connected with a pin.

Bending is a form of stress which is a combination of tensile stress and compression stress. Imagine a two-by-four stud laying across a pair of saw horses. It looks strong enough so you go sit in the middle of this piece of lumber. The fibers on the top side of the two-buy-four are being pushed together (compression) while the fibers on the bottom side are being pulled apart (tension).

Bolts and other fasteners may experience bending. This will generally happen in clevis fittings or parts cantilevered under load. If joints are too sloppy, for example, a clevis with a wide gap holding a part which may move from side to side, bending of the clevis pin may become a serious problem. This is the basic reason highly loaded fittings are manufactured to close tolerances. For the most part, the average bus nut will not have to concern himself with this type of problem. An example of a highly loaded fitting requiring close tolerance might be a landing gear attach fitting on an airplane. If the holes were a little too big, each landing cycle would cause pounding of the joint and ultimately failure due to bearing, shear or bending

Finally, we have the stress known as torsion. This is nothing more than twisting and, like all elastic materials, parts like bolts might twist and return to it's original position without failure or deformation. It is seldom we have an application on a fastener subject to torsion.

So to recap, we have five principle stresses:

1) Tension
2) Compression
3) Shear
4) Bending
5) Torsion

we did not discuss bearing stresses since they are somewhat akin to compression, but a bearing failure is a local crushing of the parent material by the fastener. Imagine what would happen if you installed a bolt into rather thin soft material. The bolt may crush the material. To avoid a bearing failure the thin material should be thickened locally where the fasteners are.

Finally mention should be made of a term we refer to as *shear tear-out*. This form of failure may be avoided by providing adequate edge distance from the line of rivets to the edge of the material to be joined. This is especially important when joining skins or thin materials. A common rule of thumb is to use an edge distance of twice the rivet diameter plus a sixteenth of an inch. If you are installing 3/16 inch diameter rivets along the edge of a piece of skin, the rivet line should be inside the edge if the skin 2 x 3/16 + 1/16 = 7/16. Any reasonable dimension greater than this would be acceptable on a bus, but not on an airplane. Airplane designers have some sort of fetish about carry unnecessary weight. As far as rivet spacing, if we have an unload siding. That is, it is only carrying it's own weight and being used for shear material, a rule of thumb might be 10 to 15 rivet diameters. In other words, you might space 3/16th inch diameter rivets from 2½ inches to 3 inches. Along the edges of the siding.

Now we have defined the basic forms of mechanical stress, (Note how I cleverly avoided physiological stress) which are push, pull, twisting, sagging and cutting (common words to describe compression, tension, torque, bending and shear). How does the average guy figure out how many rivets to put in and how often? The answer to this lies in what you are trying to hold together.

One more form of stress should be noted. That is what we call *axial stress*. In other words, pure tension and pure compression is lumped together as axial stress. How can we span a building roof without getting some sag (bending)? It can be done with axial stresses by creating a truss network. By creating a truss, such as we have seen in old bridges crossing creeks and rivers, we eliminate all bending loads and convert everything to either push or pull. The Silver Eagle is designed with much of this form of construction.

Think of a bus as a box supported at each end where the axles are. The principle stresses come from the weight of the bus and it's payload. Where the axles are attached we have a cutting action, i.e., shear. The weight also causes a sagging action between the axles: bending. And the stiffness around the box resists twisting: torque.

Getting back to the Eagle, the bending loads are resisted by the bridge like truss structure and are basically in direct stress, i.e., axial stress: compression and tension. The siding is simply a covering and designed to keep the weather out and the passengers in. Before some whiz-kid calls me a liar, the skin on the roof is essential to resist twisting and to keep the rain off. Although this is a beautifully simple structural system, it is not the lightest. But, after all, an Eagle bus does not have to fly. Still, weight affect performance such as range, payload and economy.

The drawing of the truss represents a very simple bus. The arrow marked load is the passenger. The two arrows marked reaction are the axles. By examining the design you can intuitively see the struts marked with a "C" are in compression. The structs marked with a "T"

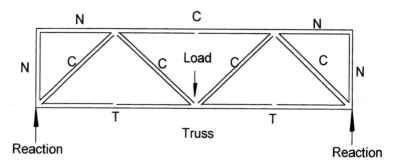

Truss

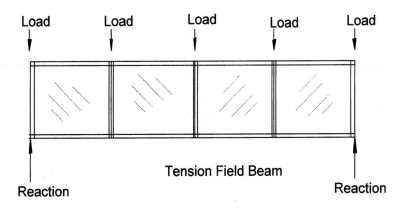

Tension Field Beam

Reaction   Reaction

are in tension, and the members marked with an"N" will have no stress in them at all. Basically a bus with many passengers simply requires a multiplication of this system and a judicious location of the struts to coincide with such things as bulkheads and axle locations.

A lighter and more sophisticated system would be to have the skin, which is necessary to keep the passenger in and the weather out, earn it's keep. This means the siding should contribute to the bending stiffness. This technique is commonly called the *stressed skin* approach, or monocoque design.

So we now have a beam to resist the bending loads instead of a truss. Obviously, an "I" beam would be suitable but heavier than the truss, so we use a beam named after the inventor, a Wagner beam.. It is also commonly referred to as a *tension field beam* . This beam has stiff top and lower chords connected with thin skin to transfer shear. The skin in one plane also stabilizes the thin stiff members so they don't buckle, or deform out of the geometry

The whole idea behind this *beam* exercise is to demonstrate how we compute the size and number of fasteners along the framework of a stresses skin. The beam shown in tension field beam illustrated will have some wrinkles in the direction shown. Additional stiffeners or thicker skin will solve this problem is it is objectionable. The principle stress we solve for is shear. Now every simple beam regardless of shape has a simple formula to determine the bending stresses and shear stresses. In the simplified case we will use the shear stresses to determine the fastener load.

$$V \text{ (shear)} = P \text{ (load)} \div 2$$

If we have a beam ten feet long and loaded at 200 lbs/foot, then our V (shear stress) is 1000 lbs/ft, or 84 lbs/inch. If we use standard 3/16 pop-rivets With a shear strength of 170 lbs per rivet, we divide $170 \div 84 = 2$ inch spacing. Actually, as we will learn later in this book, this is a very soft rivet and much stronger rivets are available.

A set of diagrams and formulae are given to demonstrate some of the more simpler stress applications. The formulae for bending stress is given although we have not gone into detail how it is used. These data are presented as reminders for those of you who were engineers but have gone to better endeavors and may have forgotten a lot of this stuff. Regardless, it's pretty useful reference material.

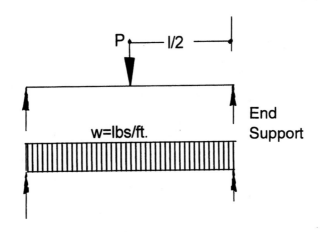

Point loading   Uniform Loading

$$\text{Max Mo} = \frac{Pl}{4}$$

$$\text{Max d} = \frac{Pl^3}{48\,EI}$$

$$V = \frac{P}{2}$$

$$\text{Max Mo} = \frac{Wl^2}{8}$$

$$\text{Max d} = \frac{5}{384}\frac{Wl^4}{EI}$$

$$V = \frac{Wl}{2}$$

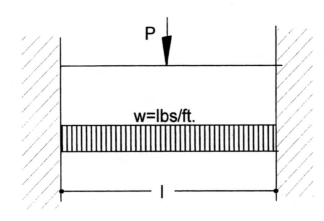

Fixed End
Support

Point Loading

Uniform Loading

$$\text{Max Mo} = \frac{Wl^2}{8}$$

$$\text{Max Mo} = \frac{Wl^2}{12}$$

$$\text{Max d} = \frac{Wl^4}{192\,E\,I}$$

$$\text{Max d} = \frac{Wl^4}{384\,E\,I}$$

$$V = \frac{Wl}{2}$$

$$V = \frac{Wl}{2}$$

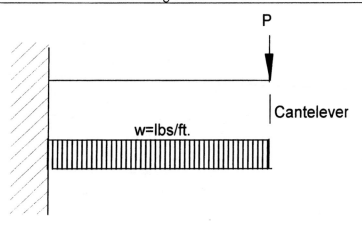

POINT LOADING

Max Mo = Pl

$$\text{Max d} = \frac{Pl^3}{3EI}$$

V = P

UNIFORM LOADING

$$\text{Max Mo} = \frac{Wl^2}{2}$$

$$\text{Max d} = \frac{Wl^4}{8EI}$$

V = Wl

The symbols in the above equations are:

Max Mo = Maximum Bending Moment in ft-lbs

l = Length of span in ft

P = Total Point Loading in Lbs.

W = weight of load in lbs/ft

V = Shear in lbs

Max d = Maximum deflection (sag)

E = Modulus of Elasticity of the material

I = Moment of inertia of the shape

The final operation in strength of materials is to select the size and material to be used for the beams.

The size and shape of the beam material determines a characteristic known as the **moment of Inertia (I)**. In simple system we use a value called the **Section Modulus (S)** which is one half the moment of inertia for simple rectangular cross sections. Finally we normally use the yield strength, or elastic limit for our limiting criteria.

With all this gobble-dee-gook in mind I will now illustrate how we use this stuff. The fiber stress in bending yields the equation : $f_b = M_o c \div I$, where $c = \frac{1}{2}$ depth of the beam. The equation may be simplified to $f_b = M_o \div S$

now we can set $f_b = 35,000$ psi (yield strength of mild steel), and solve for the section modulus (S). From the section modulus we can size our beam

I know this must read with a lot of confusion, but now I will carry it one step further and demonstrate an example.

A beam has a ten foot span and a 1,000 lbs point load in the middle and is simply supported.

Max $M_o = Pl \div 4 = 1,000 \times 120 \div 4 = 30,000$ in-lbs

I will support this with a 1 inch wide steel beam
$S = h^3 \div 6$, if $35,000$ $(f_b) = 30,000 \times 6 \div h^3$
then $h^3 = 180,000 \div 35,000 = 5.15$ inches

$h = {}^3\sqrt{5.15} = 1.74$ *inches*

If you have gotten this far, congratulations. If you fell asleep, I urge you to wake up and continue.
There really should be some interesting stuff ahead.

Notes

What's in a Nut?

Some years ago, I fell out of love with sailing and flying and became enchanted with buses. I decided to become a bus driver. Naturally, people with this form of affliction have a tendency to band together. Being a novice, I hung on every word uttered from the old timers. My background was engineering so I considered myself quite savvy, but I was just a mite confused when I heard the term *bus nut*.

I knew what a B-nut was . . . a connector for a hydraulic line. A lug nut holds a wheel on a stud. (why is it called a lug nut instead of a stud nut?) Finally I acquired a bus and was determined to find the bus nut. I snooped all over the thing and couldn't locate the damned thing. I found Acorn nuts, hex nuts, lock nuts, peanuts and even cabinets of walnuts, but no bus nut.

Enough of this nonsense! Obviously I spotted the bus nut while shaving one morning. Soon after, I discovered a whole community with this affliction. It became the custom of this group to gather once a month where the men would swap lies, drink beer and gesticulate into the rear of their coaches while their ladies would sit at tables and play cards with little rocks on them so the wind would not make them lose their places.

For some reason, this gathering place would always be somewhere nobody had been before. This was probably because people walking by would look at the group and declare, "Look at those bus nuts!" Obviously this was an insult so we always looked for a new spot to gather. I remember one time we gathered in the desert north of Victorville in California. Now this is kind of like being at the North Pole, only warmer. We only saw one old guy walking by out there and he was hollering at his burro, "Git!! Or I'll git them bus nuts on ye!"

After that experience, Ol' Mose grabbed Noah, went behind his 4104, and bemoaned, "I even saw a rattler shaking out 'bbbus nuttt'. I guess we oughta officially register ourselves as bus nuts." Now it is true. There are a lot of nuts in California. In fact some people think California is the nut capital of the world, but Noah said, "We don't have to register. The govmint gave up trying to register all the nuts in California. I do believe, however, if we are gonna be bus nuts, we should be **Bus Nuts**." Ol' Mose didn't understand the significance of Noah's statement because he couldn't see the bold capital letters, so he just thought he was being emphatic and said, "you bet! I'll drink to that!", and popped another beer.

Well, to summarize all this nonsense, this was the beginning of a great fellow and galship. These guys decided to call themselves the Bus Nuts, but then Adam pointed out there may be more who would like that name and we weren't going as far as New York City. So after much wrangling they settled on the Southwestern Bus Nuts (kind of a descriptive location from whence we are from). From this sprang the Western Bus Nuts, the Northwestern Bus Nuts, the Central Bus Nuts, the South Central Bus Nuts, the Upper US Bus Nuts, and so on, and so on.

Now there may be some who think they have prior

claim to this name, but I can prove I was the 7th president of this chapter in 1984, so I reckon 1978 was the beginning . . . nigh onto twenty years ago. I respectfully submit the above information to be true and correct to the best of my ability to remember. Of course it's said, "First thing to go is your mind." I don't remember the second thing.

Bolts

Why would anyone write about such a simple thing as bolts? After all, this is a no-brainer. You grab a bolt and if will fit in a hole and enough sticks out the other side to get a nut on it, you got it made. It clamps the parts together. If it is a vibratory condition, maybe you put a lock washer on it or a jam nut so it won't come apart. Keep in mind this book is written mainly for lawyers, doctors, accountants and sales clerks. Readers who are mechanics probably know most of this stuff and I would like to take this opportunity to thank them for buying this book regardless.

Bolts come in a wide variety of strengths and head design. The old fashioned square head will not be discussed since it has little strength and is not too common these days. The only place they are in use today is in the battery lug clamp. This is used to keep the bolt from turning while tightening the lug. Other uses may be to authenticate a restoration project.

Hex Head Bolts

The strength of hex head bolts are easily determined by the markings on the head. For the most part we will only be concerned with three SAE (Society of Automotive Engineers) grades, 2, 5, and 8. The common unmarked bolt is grade 2 made from low to medium carbon steel with a tensile strength of about 70,000 psi. The intermediate strength bolt has three radial marks on the head and is made from medium carbon steel quenched and tempered with an average tensile strength of 120,000 psi. Finally, the grade 8 bolt has 6 radial marks on the head, made from alloy steel, quenched and tempered with an average tensile strength of 150.000 psi. Obviously bolts are made which have higher strengths but are seldom used in bus fabrication. Some aircraft and engine applications use bolts which exceed 210,000 psi tensile strengths. One of the problem with very high strength steels, is brittleness. As you might imagine, a very low strength bolt is also quite ductile and may be easily deformed. As the strength increases, so does brittleness. In fact, steel can become so brittle that it will break like glass if dropped. Some of the very useful alloys are developed which have both strength and toughness. These are alloys which contain nickel and chromium and fall into the stainless steel category. The toughest alloys have molybdenum and chromium, hence the term chrome-molly steel. Many tools are made from these alloys are often referred to as tool steels.

Bolts may be classified as to their usage. For

example, tension bolts will have a very thick head for the reason the head thickness must resist in shear a direct pull on the bolt. A tension bolt may be recognized by the fact it's head is almost as thick as it's diameter. The most common bolts we will use are referred to as shear bolts. This means their application is such that the load on the bolt tends to cut through the body like a pair of scissors. The head thickness of a shear bolt is somewhat less than the body diameter.

The length of a bolt is always the distance from under the head to the end of the shank.. In other words, the head thickness does not count in the nominal length of the bolt. The length is composed of two distinct items: the grip length and the thread length. The grip length is that section of a bolt which has no threads on it, hence the thickness of material it may grip, or clamp By custom, the threads exposed after tightening a nut in place may vary but a good practice is at least one full thread and preferably three threads showing. Bolt-like fasteners less than ¼ inch are not considered bolts but are referred to as machine screws.

The following table lists the working strength of bolts. The tensile strength is limited to the area of the minimum diameter of the threads. For that reason fine thread bolts are stronger in tension than course thread bolts.

For application, a safety factor should be applied. If the load is static, a safety factor of 2 should be sufficient. If you have dynamic loading or impact loading a safety factor of 4 to 6 should be employed.

Dia	Dec.	Area	Tensile Strength			Shear Strength		
			Grd 2	Grd 5	Grd 8	Grd 2	Grd 5	Grd 8
¼	.2500	0.049	1472	3066	4416	981	2453	3680
5/16	.3125	0.076	2284	4756	6850	1522	3845	5768
⅜	.3750	0.118	3540	7384	10635	2360	5893	8850
7/16	.4325	0.137	4115	8572	12344	2743	6858	10275
½	.5000	.0.196	5888	12266	17663	3925	9813	14716
⅝	.6250	0.306	9193	18972	27578	6120	1530	22950
¾	.7500	0.442	13260	27404	39780	8840	2210	33150

When examining the number listed for shear strength the value may be doubled if the body of the bolt is in double shear. A typical example of double-shear is the use of a clevis or a shackle. A clevis demonstrates a balanced load on the bolt body, hence twice the cross sectional area of the bolt is resisting the load, ergo, double shear. A bolt may experience multiple shear strength depending on the number of shear planes on the fitting. An example of this type of loading is a finger joint with two fingers inserted into three fingers. The design would resist four times the shear capability of the bolt. Obviously, a sloppy joint could result in a failure due to something other than shear, such as bending. Therefore, in order to develop the maximum capability of the bolt, the fitting should maintain close tolerances. As you might imagine, a sloppy fit could cause pounding, jerking and adverse stresses whereas a tight fit will allow no slop therefore only the stress calculated will occur.

Socket head cap screws are more often used in tooling applications. Socket head cap screws are generally in the very high strength range such as would be classified grade 8. The socket is an Allen design and as a result can only be tightened to a minimal torque. They are quite common in molds and dies and have high strength at high temperatures.

The stove bolt is characterized by it's oval or round head. It has a square shoulder under the round head which is installed in a square hole. This allows the bolt to be tightened and prevented from turning. The strength of stove bolts is on the low order of mild steel. The stove bolt is so named since it was originally designed to assemble stoves.

Threads

SAE, that is non-metric fractional-inch, bolts come in coarse and fine thread. As a general rule, fine threaded bolts have more strength than coarse threaded bolts. It is obvious that fine threaded bolts have more capability of pure tensile strength since the threads do not reduce the diameter of the shaft as much as the coarse threads. In addition, a higher pre-stress can be applied to the fine threads, since the ramp angle of the threads is less and it takes less effort to torque the nuts.

In all fairness to foreign auto makers and our own, metric sizes are included and are for reference only. Having spent over three score plus years dealing with fractional-inch bolt sizes, the metric movement, in my mind, borders on a constipated bowel movement Maybe when I am moldering in my grave, some young buck will pick up a near ¼" bolt and declare ,"Here's a six millimeter bolt!" So much for philosophy

National Fine Threads			National Coarse Threads		
Tap size	Drill Size	Decimal	Tap size	Drill Size	Decimal
---	---	---	4-40	No 43	0.0880
---	---	---	6-32	No 36	0.1065
---	---	---	8-32	No 29	0.1360
10-32	No 21	0.1590	10-24	No 25	0.1495
---	---	---	12-24	No 16	0.1770
¼-28	No 3	0.2130	¼ - 20	No 7	0.2010
5/16-24	17/64	0.2656	5/16-18	17/64	0.2656
⅜-24	21/64	0.3281	⅜-16	5/16	0.3125
7/16-20	24/64	0.3906	7/16-14	⅜	0.3750
½-20	29/64	0.4531	½-13	27/64	0.4219

The table shown is presented so you won't have to look up the drill size for each tap in another reference book. You will note that although thread sizes from 4-40 through 12-24 are technically considered machine screws, I have included them for your convenience

AN Bolts

Perhaps many of you have heard the term *AN Bolt*. This is a designation developed for military standards. The term, *AN* refers to Army-Navy. The AN bolt is a close tolerance bolt conforming to Mil Standards. They may have a drilled shank so a lock wire may be inserted through a castellated nut. They may have a drilled head, again to accept a lock wire. And, they may also be drilled, head and shank, or not at all.

The common AN bolt sizes range from AN3 to AN8. The numbers refer to the diameter in sixteenths of an inch. In addition, the length is specified with a dash number. On average a length with a dash 10 is approximately 1 inch in length. The grip length, however, varies with the diameter. As a reminder, the grip length is the distance under the head to the beginning of the threads

The example shown below are for a cad-plated bolt ¼ inch in diameter and an overall length under the head of ¾ inch.

AN4-6	Drilled Shank
AN4-6A	Undrilled
AN4H6	Drilled Head & Shank
AN4H6A	Drilled Head

All AN bolts have national fine threads and are heat-treated cadmium plated steel with a tensile strength of 125,000 psi.

Nuts and Washers

Nuts to accommodate the various threads listed are available in several configurations. The most common nut is the simple shear nut. It is so designated since it does nothing more than hold the parts together while the application loads the bolt shank in shear. The common shear nut is normally not much thicker than the diameter of the bolt. The tension nuts is almost twice as thick as the bolt diameter. In addition, tension nuts are more common in fine threads applications since the bolt in tension should have the maximum shank diameter and the fine threads do not cut as deep into the shaft. It may be mentioned here, that some very high strength bolts have rolled threads which conform the grain of the metal to the maximum load resistance. An example of bolts such as this might be engine "head bolts", or "Jake Brake Bolts."

One of the most useful nuts around a bus is the self-locking nut with the plastic insert. This plastic is generally made of nylon and is commonly called the Ny-lock nut. Another form of nut is the castellated nut. This is a nut which has slots cut into the top of the nut so that a slot may be aligned with a hole in the bolt and a safety wire may be threaded through the hole and nut, thus preventing the nut from backing off. Another form of locking nut used extensively in the aircraft business has an extended section which is oblate, that is it is shaped like an ellipse so when it is tightened it slightly deforms the threads of the bolt and will not back off.

Exceptionally high strength nuts are used for high torque applications. Such applications might be head-bolts or Jake brake bolts and tension nuts. These take the form of the twelve point head or nut. The preponderance for head and nut design is the standard hex, also known as six points. In analyzing the load a tool such as an open end wrench applies to the nut, it is seen that there are only two bearing surfaces. By using a socket tool or a closed end wrench this increases to six bearing surfaces, which permits a higher twisting load since more surface is available for uniform load application.

When using bolts or nuts of very high strength, due to the hardness and brittleness of the material it is essential to apply the twisting load as uniformly as possible, hence the twelve point head design.

Another common nut used in vehicles is the castellated nut. This is a nut designed to be tightened to a specific location and locked into place. The nut is then lock-wired or cotter pinned at it's thread location. A form of nut used on airplanes will have a series of tangential holes drilled through so a lock wire may be threaded through and tied off at another location, thus preventing the nut from backing off

The most common device for keeping nuts in place is the split lock washer which is slightly warped to have sharp points protruding in a clockwise direction

, thus preventing a nut from turning counter-clockwise. Finally the star washer looks like a multiple pointed star with a hole and the star points are twisted to prevent a nut from backing off.

If you have a condition where it is impossible to install a lock-washer or a locknut then a chemical bonding agent is available. The most common of these is Loc-Tite. Just a tiny drop on the threads will lock a bolt in place. Often the only way to back out a bolt installed this way is to use heat. Bolts installed with a specific torque value are designed to operate without a locking device. (Note: no effort will be made here to suggest the torque values to be used when tightening a nut. In specific critical location, the manufacturer will specify that value). It is a good practice to use an anti-seize compound in these applications. An example of this might be the installation of lug nuts to hold your wheel on. It is customary to torque these nuts to 400 foot-pounds. After many months

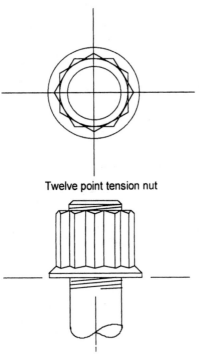

Twelve point tension nut

of all kinds of weather, corrosion may set in making removal of these nuts very difficult. An application of an anti-seize product on the studs will insure safe removal when the time comes.

Finally, washers are available for many uses. Often washers are used to provide additional clamping surface, that is spread the clamping load of the bolt over a greater surface. Plus there are body washers used to bring the surrounding material into contour and spacer washers to compensate for a hole too large, such as an electrical box and thickness washers to compensate for a bolt with too great a grip length. And, at last, there are washers in the 2" to 3: diameter range used as tokens in the Washer-toss game, sometimes known as *Polish horseshoes*. This is a game with two boards 12 feet apart with 3-2½" diameter holes into which 2" diameter washers are tossed, scored similar to horseshoes, often played at bus rallies.

A discussion of nuts would be amiss if I failed to mention Acorn-nuts. These are nuts used to finish off a connection where the nut must be expose and also be attractive. A typical example of an Acorn-nut on a bus might be the nuts holding the windshield wipers on their shafts. The chrome nut covers used on the wheel lug nuts have the appearance of an Acorn-nut. To use an Acorn nut in this application would not be practical since they would become badly scarred in use, hence the nut covers to jazz up the looks.

Screws

Screws may be classified as machine, wood, sheet metal, or drywall. The head design may be flat, oval, round, countersunk, or fillister. The application torque may be applied with a straight slot, a Phillips slot, a Torx, an Allen, or a square. So, why so many choices? Simple, every genius has to re-invent the wheel. Such a flip answer — I apologize.

Machine screws are really much like small bolts. The threads listed in the previous pages included machine screws. More and more, the Phillips design head is becoming common. With the advent of the battery operated hand drill with a Phillips screwdriver bit the installation of screws has sped up by a factor of 10 to 20. In addition, the advantage of the Phillips head, is the bit will adequately tighten the screw and not slip off the head. Furthermore, with a magnetic bit holder the fastener is held while reaching in awkward places. Many jobs which used to require a couple of guys have now become one handed.

The wood screw is an obvious choice when doing cabinet work for both assembly and installation. The drywall screw, however has become my personal choice. The drywall screw is made of hardened steel and uses threads compatible with sheet metal screws. The thread tends to deform the metal and in the process becomes self-locking.

Another advantage to the drywall screw is the size. The most common drywall screw is a number 6.

This size will self-lock in tubular steel (as most of our buses are made from) with a one-eighth inch diameter drilled hole. This allows us to screw-up a lot of material to the frame of our bus. I meant screw down rather than screw up. Another common size for drywall screws is a number seven. This too, will secure to our framework using a ⅛ inch drill bit as a pilot drill. If you use a number eight sheet metal screw as I did in my first few buses, a 9/64^{ths} inch drill bit is required in steel.

Another advantage of the drywall screw is it comes in odd lengths. For instance, 1⅜ inch length is ideal for joining a pair of ¾ inch thick wood slats and avoid piercing through and marring a finish. Another common length is 1⅝ inch. I now buy boxes of dry wall screw in boxes of 1,000 and use them for almost any application.

In this day and age when I see an old fashioned slotted head screw I pitch it into the trash bin. About the only place slotted head screw are seen now-a-days is in electrical equipment. This industry however, is slowly coming into the 21st century by including a hybrid screw head which will work with either a flat bladed screw driver or a Phillips. This way, we may install duplex receptacles and secure the cover plates with our battery operated hand drill.

Don't be chintzy when buying screws. Often screws bought from a surplus store or from a swap meet are rejected fasteners from a manufacturer or supplier. Why would they reject screws? Several reasons come to mind. If a production shop gets a batch of screws whose heads are continually twisting off, this shop will discard these screws and perhaps seek another supplier. The latest power screw drivers have a clutch so the torque may be set to drive the screw properly but will slip so as not to twist off the head Another reason screws end up at a swap meet is they are too brittle or too soft.

Locate a reputable fastener company and buy from them. In lot of 1,000 these fasteners are only a penny or two. Take my word, you may think two or three hundred screws will be all you will need; chances are you will buy more than two boxes of 1,000.

When attaching wood to wood, use flat heads screws so they may be countersunk or plugged. When attaching metal to any surface (wood or metal) use round head screws unless the metal is thick enough to counter bore or countersink.

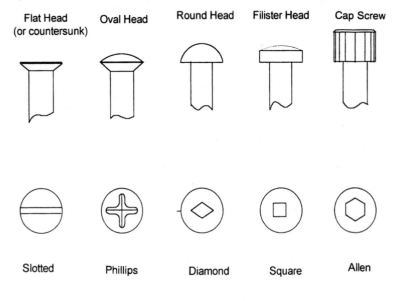

| Flat Head (or countersunk) | Oval Head | Round Head | Filister Head | Cap Screw |

| Slotted | Phillips | Diamond | Square | Allen |

Helicoils

A unique fastener is the Heli-coil™. This is a device which will permit a tapped hole with damaged threads to be repaired. Another use is to strengthen joints or allow hardened fasteners to be attached to softer materials.
Free Running Screw Thread Inserts

Characteristics

A.   Protect tapped threads against wear and damage in all metals and their alloys - aluminum, magnesium, titanium, copper, steel, as well as in plastics and other materials.

B.   They strengthen tapped threads by a more balanced distribution of dynamic and static loads for the full length of thread engagement. The flexibility of the insert compensates for lead and angle error and allows each coil to carry its share of the load.

C.   The superior corrosion resistant characteristics of HELI-COIL stainless steel inserts assure their adaptability to most materials and usual environmental. conditions. Applications must be made consistent with good engineering practice as outlined in the design engineering data. Where conditions warrant, other wire materials may be used such as phosphor bronze or lnconel X-75O.

HELI-COIL stainless steel inserts are the most widely used. They are made of 18-8 Stainless Steel to AMS 7245 and MIL-1-8846. This wire is cold rolled to a diamond cross-section producing an ultimate tensile strength
of Rc43-50) and a mirror like finish of 0.20 to 0.40 um.

D.   HELI-COIL Inserts develop maximum clamping action and bolt tension with minimum wrench torque. Their smooth rolled thread surface assures most effective use of high strength alloy steel bolts.

E.   Space saving is maximized, permitting the use of standard-boss configurations with no over-size boss required as is necessary to accommodate solid bushings. A boss Radius equal to the nominal bolt size is adequate for most load conditions.

F.   Weight saving is unmatched - an important design feature for many products, particularly airborne equipment.

G.   Cost savings apply in many directions - lower insert costs, lower installation costs and smaller bosses all produce savings.

H.   Overall product cost savings may be realized by using a less expensive material and still maintain required thread strength with HELI-COIL Inserts.

I.   Lowest installed cost is realized with HELI-COIL Power Tools and Strip Feed - production rates up to 800 or more inserts per hour with no waste.

J.   HELI-COIL Inserts provide maximum flexibility of design with the widest choice of materials for the component, the fastening, and even the insert to meet performance and production requirements.

The HELI-COIL SCREW-LOCK INSERT provides an exclusive, resilient internal locking thread that grips the bolt and prevents it from loosening under vibration or impact.

Locking action is achieved by one or more of the coils of the Insert having a series of straight segments, or chords. When the bolt enters this grip coil these chordal segments flex outward creating pressure on the bolt. This pressure is exerted between the flanks of the bolt thread thus utilizing the maximum contact area and minimizing the unit pressure.

HELI -COIL SCREW-LOCK INSERTS permit repeated assembly and disassembly, yet will not relax their grip on the screw even in tough metals such as cast iron, alloy steel, titanium, etc.

Characteristics

A.   Screw-Lock Inserts positively secure threaded members against loosening caused by vibration and shock. They have a high reusable factor due to the exclusive HELI-COIL Resilient Screw-Lock which permits frequent removal and reassembly of bolt without appreciable, loss of torque.

B.   Positive self-locking torque, complying with MIL-I-8846 & MIL-N-25027.

C.   Savings in space, weight and money, through the elimination of lock wiring, lock nuts, lock washers, chemical compounds, plastic pellets/patches and other locking mechanisms. In addition Screw-Lock Screw Thread Inserts have all the characteristics of Free Running Inserts

How To Install A Heli-Coil Screw Thread Insert

(1) Drill
Drill out the damaged threads using the drill size specified in the catalog. Drill to sufficient depth to accommodate the insert length and bolt or screw being used.
(2) Tap
Use the Heil-Coil Tap specified in the catalog. Check the size on your shank to make sure you have the right one. Tap the hole to sufficient depth to accommodate the insert
length and bolt or screw being used.
(3) Install
Use the installation tool specified in the catalog. Just wind the insert into the hole until the top coil is 1/4-1/2

turn into the tapped thread.

Note: Remove tang with the appropriate tool specified.

Notes

Things to Cry Over
(And you will)

Many of you reading this book are retired teachers, accountants, UPS drivers, golf instructors and anything but accomplished and skilled craftsmen. For those of you having mechanical talents, your purchase is greatly appreciated.

Fasteners have a habit of not doing what they are instructed to do. Especially if the moon is in the fifth quarter and you are sharing a six pack with a buddy. What follows is a list of common fastener misbehavior and what you should do about them.

1. You have carefully pre-drilled a fine piece a hardwood which will be exposed. As you are driving a screw into this fine piece of material, the head shears off.

If you are lucky, the head sheared off with an eighth-inch of shank exposed allowing you to vice-grip the shank and back it out. If the head sheared below the surface (and this is the normal case), use a sledge hammer(as heavy as you can lift) with a punch and drive it deeper. Then, drill it for a plug and glue in a plug and sand .flush. Don't bother to install another screw since the one already buried is doing all you can expect it to.

2. You are tightening a bolt and the head twists off.
    Simple, replace the bolt.

3. You are tightening a nut on a stud and the stud twists

Uh ohh! In this case you have little choice but to drill and try to use an Easy-out. Sometimes it is necessary to carefully drill with a body drill and re-tap the threads. If the stud is welded it will have to be removed and new one in it's place.

4. You have carefully drilled and countersunk a series of hole in a brass (or stainless steel) piano hinge. Now you are ready to install it. It's 38 feet long and you have installed 32,428 brass flush head screws with only one to go. As the last screw is sinking to complete the kob, the head twists off. What will you do?

a. You try to drill out the broken screw

b. You add another countersunk hole adjacent thus spoiling the looks of your job

c. You politely scream some deleted expletives.

d. You open a beer

e. You take up knitting

Answer: none of the above, you simply cry a lot.

5. You are using one of those aircraft drills that are one-eighth inch in diameter and six inches long creating a pilot hole. Your son's girl friend walks by in a bikini. You hear a snap and discover an inch of the drill is protruding out the other side of your wrist. What do you do?

This one is easy, you reverse the drill and back it out of your wrist. You will notice, however, you have no feeling in your middle finger.

6. Probably the commonest fastener misbehavior is the bending of a nail while in the process of being driven.

This form of deviation is easily analyzed. Once the nail has begun to penetrate the material, the slightest degree of striking-load eccentricity from normal (normal being defined as the alignment axis of the nail) will cause a bending-moment and subsequent catastrophic failure of the shaft of the nail. This will cause a resultant bendment of the nail thus rendering the fastener badly out of shape. Pull it out and start over with a virgin (unsullied) nail.

7. A staple whether air driven or spring driven is an embarrassment when it misses it's target. Now, this is a no-brainer!. How can a guy miss his target with a staple? It is pushing against the part, isn't it? Well, I'm here to tell you a staple has it's own directivity. If you put the gun against your target but are not careful to point it normal (normal being defined as perpendicular), it will fire and come out the side of your cabinet, creating much consternation and chagrin.

The common solution is a pair of dikes to grab the offending leg and wiggle it until it breaks off. Sometimes the staple may be stiff enough to be driven backwards out of the part. This is, however, seldom successful. Keep a can of matching Famowood (a sandable/stainable wood putty).

8. A bolt too long is such a simple problem,

Go buy one the right size. Or, grab a handful of

washers and build up the stack until the bolt is not too long. Or.. .. , get out your die set, using the appropriate cutter, mill some more threads on your bolt and cut the excess threads off.

9. You need to clamp some parts together but only have a bolt much smaller in diameter than needed.. This is too dumb to discuss.

10. You have selected an ideal location to install a part to the frame of your bus. Just as you complete the pilot hole into the frame the drill breaks off flush with the frame surface.

At this point, there are several solutions.

a. Calmly stand up, go to the nearest brick wall and beat your head for 60 seconds.

b. After your blood pressure has returned to 250 over 150, analyze the wisdom of your original location.

c. Try and find your needle nose pliers and discover they are too thick at the points to do any good.

d. Sharpen a hardened scribe or punch with a grinding wheel and beat on the broken drill until it falls into the framework to forever dwell there. Then clean out the hole with a new drill and proceed. Put a few band-aids on your forehead.

11. What is more common than a hex-head bolt with rounded corners? The bolt is stubborn so you get a cheater on the wrench and waa-laa, the wrench simply

rotates around the head but the bolt stays where it is.

The logical solution is to get a pair of three foot Vice Grips, grab the head and twist it off, since the bolt still would not come loose. Ahhh, but what if the bolt head is shielded so all you can use is a socket wrench? And to add to the problem, the damned head is metric and all you have are SAE sockets?

(Actually, this is how the points on the head became rounded in the first place.) It may become necessary to get out the center punch and drill. Begin with a small drill bit and gradually work up until the head leaves the bolt.

Actually, several other tricks are available such as penetrating oil with vibration and heat. But these are too straight forward.

12. The next example is the opposite of the previous discussion. You are removing a series of Phillips head screws with a power screw-driver (or by hand. . . It doesn't matter) when the head of the screw suddenly becomes a beautifully rounded conic depression thus rendering the screw-un-driver useless.. By the way, this works both directions. (And, I might add parenthetically, stainless steel screws are terrible in this respect. They are made from 302 stainless and are dead soft. Do not exert too much torque with your driver or you will have un-screw able screws.)

Getting back to the solution above, it should be an easy matter to drill out the old screw since it was pretty soft in the first place

13. Another common fastener problem is while mounting a light, or some part, the screw penetrates a buried electrical wire and shorts out a circuit.

The solution is to remove the screw and pray the short goes away

14. How about drilling into a water cavity or a buried pipe.
I once lost a car engine because a mechanic mounting an air conditioning compressor drilled into a water jacket to install a stud.

There is not a happy answer to this problem. Just remember what Forrest Gump once said.

15. You've got a screw loose. Now, this is a given if you are messing around with buses.

How do you tighten up a loose screw? If it is in metal, you might try injecting the hole with silicone or epoxy. If it is wood, the old fashioned way was to break off a piece of kitchen match and stuff it into the hole and re-install the screw. A lot of old tome carpenters kept a pocket of kitchen matches to light their cigarettes and fill holes with loose screws. Both kitchen matches and cigarettes are becoming scarce these days, so a whittled sliver will do the job.

16. How about a loose rivet?

Rivets loosen because of pounding and poor fit to begin with. Make sure you rivets have the proper grip length and the proper diameter. Ir's O.K. to drill a hole 1/64th oversize for a rivet since it swells when upsetting. Anymore than that, however, and the rivet will become loose. Drill, or drive out the old rivet and reinstall with a larger body diameter or one of the proper grip length.

17. What about a rust streak from a rivet?

Get rid of this rivet. Drive the pin through and install a rivet of the same metal. This means a mandrel (pin)and body of aluminum or stainless steel. If you have any aluminum rivets with steel mandrels (pin, or nails as some call them), toss them and ban them from your stock.

Editor's Note: Every one of the items listed above has happened to the hapless author.

Notes

Rivet Revelations

Very little has to be said as to what a rivet is. However, a rivet does have some unique properties. To cite a ridiculous example, what if an airplane's skin was bolted in place instead of riveted. Each bolt hole would have to be very close tolerance and the installation of the bolts would be very time consuming and have to have lock nuts securing the bolts. Otherwise, the bolts would loosen and the holes would elongate and eventually the siding would tear and cause a catastrophic failure. Rivets have the unique characteristic of entering a hole with a small degree of misalignment and/or oversize, yet when bucked, upset, or pulled, expand inside the holes to completely fill the cavity. In addition, rivets will, in the process of being set, not only fill the holes completely, but clamp, or draw, the materials together.

Some rivets are more adept at one thing or the other. This is why so many configurations are available. It is seldom we have the opportunity to use the common bucked rivets since it requires one person to use the air hammer and another person to use the bucking tool. Also, access to the bucked side is necessary. More often, we are attaching material to rectangular tubing without access to the inside of the tube. Consequently, the blind, or pull type rivet is our choice.

The most common and least expensive of blind rivets are the POP rivet. POP is the original blind rivet manufacturer. As a blind fastener, it may be inserted and set from one side of the workpiece. And while unique benefits are obtained through this feature, POP applications are not limited to blind holes. In fact, Pop blind rivets are increasingly found in both blind and non-blind applications as a replacement for welds, adhesives, screws, nuts and bolts, etc.

The ability to set Pop rivets without the need for access at the back of the work makes their use mandatory in many instances. However, their many additional advantages make Pop rivets the logical choice in numerous applications where the blind-setting feature is not of primary importance. Following are some of these important Pop rivet advantages compared with conventional fasteners

Real or "in-place" costs are often lower than those of other fasteners because of their speed and ease of application.

Fast assembly: Because Pop rivets can be set in seconds. Literally.

Low-cost, lightweight, easily portable tools: Manual or power tools are easy to take to the work ... reduce operator fatigue ... and minimize capital expenditure.

Strong, reliable fastenings, independent of operator skill: Pop rivets don't torque out like threaded fasteners, wasting time and material. Correct setting pressure is predetermined by the breaking point designed into the mandrel. So you get uniformly strong, reliable fastenings the first time ... all the time.

Vibration-proof assembly: Pop rivets won't back

out or vibrate loose and fall out like threaded fasteners.

No surface marring: Setting tool won't slip and mar polished or finely finished surfaces. No dents, dimpling , or wrench marks.

Exceptional versatility: Pop rivets hold securely in thin or thick, soft or hard materials, ideal for dissimilar materials. First choice for plastics and other easily damaged components.

High grip and pull-up strengths: A Pop rivet draws parts together, even when a gap exists between parts.

Tamper-proof: Ideal where tampering and vandalism are problems. Excellent for fastening limited-access panels; authorized personnel with correct equipment easily drill out Pop rivets and replace in seconds.

Increased design flexibility: Setting without need for access at back, minimum back-up space requirements, versatility, and neat appearance are just a few of the Pop rivet attributes that contribute to design flexibility and improve the quality of the finished product

Head Styles

Dome Head Rivet

With its neat appearance and low profile, this is the most versatile and most commonly specified head style. The dome head has twice the diameter of the rivet body, providing enough bearing surface to retain all but extremely soft or brittle materials. Available in a very wide range of materials.

Large Flange Rivet

Large Flange Pop rivets have twice the under-head bearing surfaces of comparable dome head rivets and are designed for applications where soft or brittle materials must be assembled to a rigid backing material.

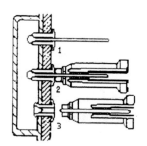

Countersunk Rivet

This head design is specified wherever a flush surface is required. Available in a variety of sizes and materials.

Applications

The low-profile dome head is appropriate for most applications. However, when soft or brittle materials are fastened to a rigid backing member, the large flange head should be considered, because it offers twice the bearing. surface. Where a flush surface is required, the countersunk head style should be selected.

How Do They Work?

A blind rivet consists of two parts: the rivet body and, within it, the setting mandrel. As shown in the accompanying drawing:
(1) The rivet body is inserted in a hole in the materials to be joined.

(2) The tool is actuated and the jaws of the power-operated or manual POP Rivet tool grip the mandrel of the rivet.

(3) The rivet is set by pulling the mandrel head into the rivet body, expanding it, and forming a strong, tight, reliable joint. At a predetermined setting force, the mandrel breaks and falls away.

Rivet Selection: Factors To Consider
1. Joint strength

First determine the single-joint tensile and shear values required for the application. These are functions of total joint strength, fastener spacing, rivet body material and rivet diameter. Then refer to the "Shear" and "Tensile" columns on the product, and select a Pop rivet that provides the values required. *"POP" brand rivets are not certified for structural aerospace applications and such use is not recommended.*

2. Joint thickness

Measure the total thickness of the materials to be joined. This determines the required "grip" of the rivet you select. Refer to the "Grip Range" column and select a rivet with a grip range that includes the work thickness required. Remember that insufficient rivet length will not allow proper formation of the secondary head at the back of the work.

3. Nature of materials

Both the rivet and the materials to be fastened will affect the ultimate joint strength. As a general rule, the rivet materials should have the same physical and mechanical properties as the materials to be fastened, because a marked dissimilarity may cause joint failure due either to material fatigue or galvanic corrosion.

4. Hole size

Hole size can be important in blind riveting. Too small a hole will, of course, make rivet insertion difficult. Too large a hole will reduce the shear and tensile strengths and it may even cause bulging or separation of the members by allowing the rivet to expand between them instead of on the blind side. Best practice is to follow the hole size recommendations provided. Also, avoid burrs in and around the holes.

5. Head Style:

The low-profile dome head is appropriate for most applications. However, when soft or brittle materials are fastened to a rigid backing member, the large flange head should be considered, because it offers twice the bearing. surface. Where a flush surface is required, the countersunk head style should be selected.

The table below lists the diameters available and typical tensile and shear values for the combination of rivet bodies and mandrel materials. The material abbreviations are:

Alum = Aluminum   Stl = Steel   Cpr = Copper
Nick = Nickel   Zinc = Zinc   SS= Stainless Steel
The values given are in pounds.

The Cherry rivet is another common expression

for a blind rivet. Cherry is a division of Textron, Inc., and makes a variety of blind rivets as does POP. Some Cherry rivets meet Mil Standards and are approved for use on aircraft and military applications. These are referred to as .MS rivets and are mentioned for reference only. The Cherry rivets discussed in the following pages are considered commercial fasteners.

The table below is a list of the various commercial rivet products available from Cherry:

Non-Structural

Nail Rivet	AA, BS, SS, MS, CS, CC, US
Cherry E Rivet	AS, AC
Cherry C Rivet	AS, SS, CS
Softset Rivet	LB
Splined Rivet	SS
CherryMate ® Rivet	BA, BS, SS
NS KlampTite® Rivet	BA

Structural

Cherry Q® Rivet	AA, BS, SS, MS, CS, CC
Cherry T Rivet	BA, BS
Multi-grip T Rivet	BS
Monobolt Rivet	BA, SS, CC
VariGrip® Rivet	BA
KlampTite® Rivet	BA

The first .letter above designates the rivet body material and the second letter designates the stem, or mandrel material.

A = Aluminum   B = Al #5056
L = Aluminum #1100   C = Stainless Steel
M = Monel   S = Steel
U = Copper

For further reference, a catalog may be obtained from Cherry Division of Textron, 1224 E. Warner Ave. Box 2157 Santa ana, CA 92707-0157, (714)540-979-2121.

For our purposes, I will only discuss three specific rivet types most useful for the bus conversion specialist, you, my reader. These will be the T rivet, the monobolt and the Varigrip® rivet.

T-Rivet

The "T" rivet comes in 3/16 inch diameter and 1/8 inch diameter. It is available in BA series (5056 Al w/Al mandrel) and BS series (5056 AL w/Steel mandrel)

The 3/16" diameter has 800 lbs shear and 500 lbs tensile strength in the BA series. In the BS series it's shear strength is 1000 lbs and tensile strength is 600 lbs.

The 1/4" diameter has 1400 lbs shear and 1000lbs tensile strength in the BA series. In the BS series it's shear strength is 1900 lbs and tensile strength is1100 lbs.

The "T" rivet features:

Extremely high shear and tensile strength. The hardened mandrel in the "T" rivet provides high tensile strength and shear values comparable solid aluminum rivets or machine screws.

High Clamp up . The "T" rivet will draw sheets firmly together, even when separated by as much as 3/16".

Mechanically Locked Mandrel. The "T" rivet will withstand severe vibration without the loss of the mandrel's plug section.

The "T" rivet is my personal choice for installing new caps on bus bodies. Often fiberglass caps will have a little deformation due to creep. That is after leaving the mould and being stored for a while, some slight change in shape will occur in fiberglass sections. This will necessitate a drawing back into contour when installing.

The "T" rivet is ideal for this ,in that it's mandrel has three points on the head and while it is being set, these points cause three leaves to curl back exerting a high clamping pressure, bring the parts together. In addition, the mandrel head is locked in position adding to the shear material.

Diameter	Stress	Al/AL	St/St	SS/SS
3/16"	Tension	450	1000	1000
	Shear	550	1300	1300
1/4"	Tension	830	1850	1850
	Shear	1270	2400	2400

Monobolt Rivet

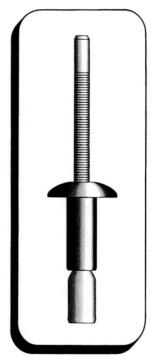

The monobolt rivet is available in three material combinations, all aluminum, all steel and all stainless steel. It is also available in 3/16 inch diameter and 1/4 inch diameter and the three material listed. The table below give the shear and tensile strength in the various options.

The monobolt has extra high shear and tensile strength as shown in the table above. This allows fewer rivets per structure at a lower installed cost.

It has excellent clamp-up characteristics. It pulls the sheets together consistently.

Since the monobolt is a wire drawn rivet, it expands radially during setting completely

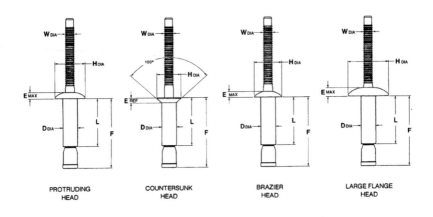

PROTRUDING HEAD   COUNTERSUNK HEAD   BRAZIER HEAD   LARGE FLANGE HEAD

NOM. RIVET DIAM.	HOLE SIZE AND DRILL NUMBER	W MAND. DIAM.	D RIVET DIAM.	PROTRUDING HEAD		LARGE FLANGE HEAD		BRAZIER HEAD		COUNTERSUNK HEAD	
				H HEAD DIAM.	E HEAD THICK.	H HEAD DIAM.	E HEAD THICK.	H HEAD DIAM.	E HEAD THICK.	H HEAD DIAM.	E HEAD THICK.
3/16	.191-.201 (#11)	.118	.187	.375	.085	.515	.100	–	–	.335	.070
1/4	.261-.276 (17/64")	.157	.257	.500	.112	–	–	.469	.094	.405	.079

filling even elliptical holes. This provide resistance to vibration and leakage. As a result it seals the hole.

Finally, when being set the mandrel breaks off flush with the surface of the head, providing the proper grip length is used for the combined material thicknesses.

The illustrations shows the various configurations available

Varigrip Rivet

The Varigrip™ rivet by Cherry is only made with 5056 aluminum body with an aluminum mandrel and in diameters of 3/16 inch and 1/4 inch. The 3/16 inch diameter has a shear value of 675 lbs. And a tensile capability os 400 lbs. The 1/4 inch diameter has a shear capability of 1350 lbs. And a tensile value of 850 lbs.

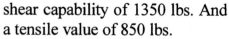
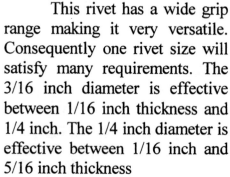

This rivet has a wide grip range making it very versatile. Consequently one rivet size will satisfy many requirements. The 3/16 inch diameter is effective between 1/16 inch thickness and 1/4 inch. The 1/4 inch diameter is effective between 1/16 inch and 5/16 inch thickness

The mandrel breaks flush with the head throughout the grip range, so there is no need to trim.

This rivet has a large blind side footprint. The body splits into four "petals" to form a large footprint creating greater holding strength.

During installation, the VariGrip rivet pulls the material firmly together prior to the rivet locking in place. The rivet body also expands radially to completely fill the hole, thus assuring tremendous reliability.

This is the rivet of choice for all round adaptability and economy.

Caps

As mentioned earlier, The Cherry style rivets (T rivet, monobolt and VariGrip) are designed so the mandrel (stem) breaks flush with the head. This feature is such that no further effort need be made for cosmetics.

This is not true of the common Pop rivet. After setting the Pop rivet shows a hole down the middle of each rivet. Over a period this rivet might loosen due to working and flexing since there is no material inside the rivet body and it is effectively a tube. In addition, it looks kind of funny to see a series of fasteners with holes down their middle.

As a result the rivet cap was developed. The cap is a small mushroom with a stem slightly larger than the hole in the rivet and a smooth cap. A tool must be used to set the cap. It is a punch with a concave face fitting the contour of the cap and is used to drive the caps into the body of the rivet.

By installing these caps, two things result. First the appearance is greatly enhanced and all the rivets appear as normal bucked rivets. Second, by driving the stem into the hole in the body of the rivet, the shear strength is increased and the vibration resistance is enhanced by expanding the body of the rivet into the hole more. These caps are made by other manufacturers then POP and are normally about 2 to 3 cents apiece

It must be emphasized that caps can only be installed on rivets attached to rigid framework. Attempts to install caps on rivets attaching siding to siding will result in deformation of the siding since it is necessary to use a punch to set the caps.

Shavehead Rivets

One form of rivet needing a brief discussion is the shavehead rivet. The is a pull type rivet. That is a blind rivet installed from one side. The shavehead rivet comes in two diameters; 3/16 inch and 1/4 inch. The grip length is the same for both sizes and ranges from .050 inch to .500 inch. The 3/16 rivet has a shear strength of 740 lbs with a tensile strength of 450 lbs. The 1/4 inch rivet has a shear strength of 1100 lbs and a tensile strength of 675 lbs.

This rivet has three slots milled down the sides of the body. When it is set, the three segments fold out like petals, thus clamping the parts together. After the rivet is set, the protruding mandrel is nipped flush with a pair of "dikes", or side nippers. The shaver tool is installed in an ordinary 1/4 drill motor and shaves the rivet head to give the appearance of solid rivets. The clamp-up power of the shavehead rivet compares to the compression of a fully torqued nut and bolt.

These rivets may be obtained from J. Byler Rivet Supply, Inc. P.O. Box 154093, Irving, TX 75015, 1(800)325-3147.

Rivet Tools

In addition to the shavehead rivet tool mentioned above, the common hand rivet setting tool and the power rivet setting tool will be described.

The hand rivet setting tool for a blind rivet is composed of a stationary tip, a set of gripping jaws and a pair of handles to retract the jaws. The tip slips over the rivet mandrel and as the jaws are retracted, they grip the mandrel and pull it through the rivet body.

After a few dozen rivets pulled by hand, a person is ready to plunge their hands in ice, or wrap them around a cold beer. An air operated rivet gun makes this job easy and simple.

Air operated rivet guns can be very expensive, such as two to three hundred dollars. If you plan to do production work, however, they are well worth it. An inexpensive air/hydraulic rivet gun is imported from Taiwan and is quite satisfactory for limited work as needed by the self conversion specialist. These tools sell for a bout $50.

My personal experience over the past ten years, or so, is to use the cheap imported knock-off. It has worked well for re-siding buses and installing caps. And, in that time I am only on my fourth gun. Sometimes being cheap can be expensive.

These guns operate on the air over hydraulic principle (shown below). A 2½ inch diameter air piston with 100 psi will exert about 500 pounds against a ¼ inch diameter hydraulic piston which will in turn exert a

10,000 pound pull. The stroke length is less than an inch and this load will cause the mandrel to break at a predetermined load and position.

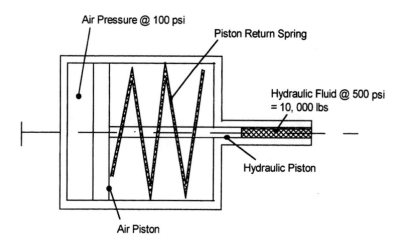

Conclusions

R ivets take many forms. Obviously we will not discuss the copper rivets used to terminate the seams in a pair of Jeans. Suffice it to say a rivet is any permanent fastener clinched into material.   T h e comparative cost of rivets are:

Pop rivets	about 3 to 4 cents
Monobolts	about 11 to 15 cents
T Rivets	about 12 cents
VariGrip	about 10 cents

The figures given above will depend upon the quantity bought. In one fastener store I saw Monobolts in quantities of 100 priced at 27 cents each, whereas if they are purchased in a box of 5,000 they sell for about 11 cents each.. Pop rivets in most industrial supply stores currently sell for about $15.00 for a box of 500. Keep in mind, the price varies according to the size, the grip length and the head configuration. Rivet caps are about $20 for a box of 1,000.

Notes

Welding

Welding, in engineering, is any process in which two or more pieces of metal are joined together by the application of heat, pressure, or a combination of both. Most of the processes may be grouped into two main categories: pressure welding, in which the weld is achieved by pressure; and heat welding, in which the weld is achieved by heat. Heat welding is the most common welding process used today. Brazing and soldering are other means of joining metals.

With the development of new techniques during the first half of the 20th century, welding replaced bolting and riveting in the construction of many types of structures, including bridges, buildings, and ships. It is also a basic process in the automotive and aircraft industries and in the manufacture of machinery. Along with soldering and brazing, it is essential in the production of virtually every manufactured product involving metals.

The welding process best suited to joining two pieces of metal depends on the physical properties of the metals, the specific use to which they are applied, and the production facilities available. Welding processes are generally classified according to the sources of heat and pressure used.

The original pressure process was forge welding. Forge welding was practiced for centuries by blacksmiths and other artisans. The metals are brought to a suitable temperature in a furnace, and the weld is achieved by hammering or other mechanical pressure. Forge welding is used rarely in modern manufacturing.

The welding processes most commonly employed today include gas welding, arc welding, and resistance welding. Other joining processes include Thermit welding, laser welding, and electron-beam welding.

Gas Welding

Gas welding is a nonpressure process using heat from a gas flame. The flame is applied directly to the metal edges to be joined and simultaneously to a filler metal in wire or rod form, called the welding rod, which is melted to the joint. Gas welding has the advantage of involving equipment that is portable and does not require an electric power source. The surfaces to be welded and the welding rod are coated with flux, a fusible material that shields the material from air, which would result in a defective weld.

Arc Welding

Arc-welding processes, which have become the most important welding processes, particularly for joining steels, require a continuous supply of either direct or alternating electrical current. This current is used to create an electric arc, which generates enough heat to melt metal and create a weld

Arc welding has several advantages over other welding methods. Arc welding is faster because of its high heat concentration, which also tends to reduce distortion in the weld. Also, in certain methods of arc welding, fluxes are not necessary. The most widely used arc-welding processes are shielded metal arc, gas-tungsten arc, gas-metal arc, and submerged arc.

Shielded Metal Arc

In shielded metal-arc welding, a metallic electrode, which conducts electricity, is coated with flux and connected to a source of electric current. The metal to be welded is connected to the other end of the same source of current. By touching the tip of the electrode to the metal and then drawing it away, an electric arc is formed. The intense heat of the arc melts both parts to be welded and the point of the metal electrode, which supplies filler metal for the weld. This process, developed in the early 20th century, is used primarily for welding steels.

Gas-Tungsten Arc

In gas-tungsten arc welding, a tungsten electrode is used in place of the metal electrode used in shielded metal-arc welding. A chemically inert gas, such as argon, helium, or hydrogen, is used to shield the metal from oxidation. The heat from the arc formed between the electrode and the metal melts the edges of the metal. Metal for the weld may be added by placing a bare wire in the arc or the point of the weld. This process can be used with nearly all metals and produces a high-quality weld. However, the rate of welding is considerably slower than in other processes.

Gas-Metal Arc

In gas-metal welding, a bare electrode is shielded from the air by surrounding it with argon or carbon dioxide gas or by coating the electrode with flux. The electrode is fed into the electric arc, and melts off in droplets to enter the liquid metal that forms the weld. Most common metals can be joined by this process.

Submerged Arc

Submerged-arc welding is similar to gas-metal arc welding, but in this process no gas is used to shield the weld. Instead, the arc and tip of the wire are submerged beneath a layer of granular, fusible material formulated to produce a proper weld. This process is very efficient but is generally only used with steels.

Resistance and Thermit Welding

In resistance welding, heat is obtained from the resistance of metal to the flow of an electric current. Electrodes are clamped on each side of the parts to be welded, the parts are subjected to great pressure, and a heavy current is applied briefly. The point where the two metals meet creates resistance to the flow of current. This resistance causes heat, which melts the metals and creates the weld. Another name for this type of welding is known as *flash* welding. Resistance welding is extensively employed in many fields of sheet metal or wire manufacturing and is particularly adaptable to repetitive welds made by automatic or semiautomatic machines. A common example of this is fabrication of bandsaw blades.

In Thermit welding, heat is generated by the chemical reaction that results when a mixture of aluminum powder and iron oxide, known as Thermit, is ignited. The aluminum unites with the oxygen and generates heat, releasing liquid steel from the iron. The liquid steel serves as filler metal for the weld. Thermit welding is employed chiefly in welding breaks or seams in heavy iron and steel sections. It is also used in the welding of rail for railroad tracks.

New Processes

The use of electron beams and lasers for welding has grown during the second half of the 20th century. These methods produce high-quality welded products at a rapid rate. Laser welding and electron-beam welding have valuable applications in the automotive and aerospace industries.

Brazing

Brazing, is a method of joining two metal surfaces by using nonferrous filler metal heated to above 430° C (800° F), but below the melting point of the metals to be joined. The kinds of filler metal used include brass, bronze, or a silver alloy; the filler metal distributes itself between the surfaces to be bonded by capillarity. Brazing is different from welding; in welding, partial melting of the surfaces may occur, and the filler metal is not distributed by capillarity. Brazing differs from ordinary soldering only in the temperature of the operation; ordinary, or soft, solder melts at temperatures below 430° C, but brazing alloys, sometimes called hard solder, melt above that temperature.

In general, brazing requires careful cleaning of the surfaces to be joined and the use of flux, such as borax, to reduce any oxide film on the surfaces. In mass production, furnaces are often used to heat the parts to be brazed, or the parts are brazed by dipping in baths of molten filler alloys. For single, non-repetitive operations, the joint is usually heated with a gas, oxyacetylene, or oxyhydrogen torch.

Soldering

Solder, any of several metallic alloys that melt at comparatively low temperatures and are used for the patching or joining of metals. Solders are commonly classified as soft and hard solders, depending upon their melting points and strengths. Soft solders are alloys of lead and tin, sometimes with the addition of bismuth; hard solders are alloys of silver, copper, and zinc (silver solder) or of copper and zinc (brazing spelter).

In joining two pieces of metal with solder, the joining surfaces are first cleaned mechanically and then coated with a flux, usually of rosin or borax, that cleans them chemically and assists the solder in making a bond. The surfaces are then heated, either with a hot metal tool called a soldering iron or soldering copper or with some form of alcohol or gas blowtorch. When the surfaces are heated to the melting point of the solder, the solder is applied and runs freely, solidifying as the surfaces cool. In the form of soldering known as sweating, the pieces to be joined are first coated individually with solder and then clamped together and heated to form the finished joint. Soldering is not significantly different from brazing and welding, except that soldering metals and alloys used for joining have less physical strength and lower boiling points.

Notes

Metal Joining for Bus Converters

The foregoing discussion is basically what you might read in an encyclopedia. How does all this apply to the standard backyard conversion specialist? This could the subject of a complete volume, however, I will attempt to enlighten the reader with my personal experience.

To begin with, welding does not have the strength of the parent material. The weld zone is, for all practical purposes, a casting. The parent metal may be hot rolled or cold rolled steel. In any event it is worked metal which tends to align the grain of the metal in the direction of the principal loading, thus causing the material to have more resistance to failure.

To illustrate my meaning, a forging hammers and works the metal so the grain is aligned with the principal loading, creating the highest strength possible in a shape. A weldment, that is, a part which might substitute for a forging, will not have the same strength as a forging, but be much stronger than a casting. This is because the elements which make up the weldment will be rolled shapes attached and oriented in the direction of the principal stresses. The weak link, however, will be the weld zones. These zones are equivalent in strength to a casting.

Another critical item in welding is oxidation. It is important to shield the weld zone from the air, which of course is composed of oxygen. A weld zone with oxidization is subject to cracks, cold-shuts and porosity, resulting in a weak, brittle weld which may leak if in a gas or liquid environment. As an example, you may make a weld with a wire-feed machine (also known as a MIG [metalic inert gas]) without the gas but you are risking the type of condition just described. Another fault with a weld zone is called hydrogen embrittlement caused by moisture in the air. The condition of hydrogen embrittlement is a guarantee of ultimate failure, especially in a moving load environment.

Several types of inert gases are available at all welding supply stores. CO_2, or carbon dioxide is the least expensive, but throughly adequate for the average Busnut. A mixture of Argon and Carbon dioxide is next in line. The highest quality is Argon, but it is also quite expensive. Other inert gases are nitrogen, used to flood the tops of containers such as paint, so as to avoid a skin on the material and helium.

The Buzz Box

The little AC/DC Lincoln arc welder is affectionately know as the *buzz box* . This welder is probably the staple of the home workshop welders. It is adjustable from 75 amps to 120 amps in click stop settings of 15 amps. For the ordinary bus frame modification welding 3/32 inch diameter rod is suitable for most applications.

Arc welding rods, which are coated with a fusible ceramic flux come in various grades, alloys, and diameters. The designation 6011 is, in my opinion, the most universally useable grade. This rod allows one to weld dirty materials along with some degree of rust. The 3/32 inch diameter rod will weld from .100 inch thick material up to 3/16 inch thick material in one pass. Thinner material may be successfully welded with lower heat and a great deal of care. For thicker materials, multiple passes will be necessary. The weld zone must be cleaned of the glass like deposit from the weld rod shielding material. A chipping hammer is available for this purpose. The weld zone should preferably be ground clean before another pass is made. All voids and flux inclusions should be removed before re-welding. (*Editors note: how do you remove a void?*) [*Authors's note: Don't ask!*]

Probably the biggest single deterrent keeping all of us from becoming certified welders, besides the fact we need to make a living, is the ability to see in the dark. Of course, if you have Parkinson's disease, this may also be a handicap. However, all good welders must be able to either see in the dark through a number 10 lens, or have a pretty good idea where his weld zone is in a blind condition. Gas welding does not need near the eye protection arc welding demands. A good pair of really dark sunglasses seems to work OK for gas welding, but the arc is so bright when arc welding, a minimum of a number 10 lens is necessary or eye damage will occur.

Old guys (and most of us are, or will be) also have another handicap: they wear bi-focal glasses. So, the standard welding helmet with it's 2" x 4" lens requires a neck bend to end all neck bends. The answer is a helmet with a big 4½" x 5" lens. An ideal solution would be a face shield with a dark enough color, but face shields are not made for arc welding since the spatter can be really nasty. One neat helmet has a flipper lens operated with the welder's chin. He holds the lens open with his chin and positions his stinger, then closes his mouth closing the lens and strikes his arc.

A professional welder will wear leather gloves, sleeves and probably leather chaps and apron. Almost all of us backyard conversion specialists who have done any welding will have our share of holes burned in our jeans and socks. Never, never weld without eye protection and gloves. And, brown cotton Mickey Mouse gloves are disqualified except for gas welding

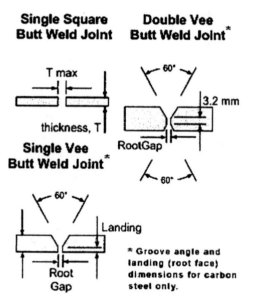

An essential pair of tools for any welder besides his welding machine is a hand held grinder and a wire brush. A power driven wire brush is preferable.

The proper material preparation for welding is essential and is a subject all it's own. Only the rudimentary facts will be included. The expression *penetration* is as important in welding as it is in sex. Without proper penetration the joint is poor and the relationship will probably fail. *(Editor's Note: Please excuse the author, He thought he was Dr. Ruth momentarily).*

We have all seen welds which look like bubble gum stuck to the part. More often than not, these welds are only partial welds. They will have some, but not all the parent metal melted and fused to the filler metal and the adjoining part. The biggest problem with bubble-gum welding is, it not only looks bad, the partial penetration will cause stress-risers, i.e., stress concentration points, and partial embrittlement and guarantee failure. The drawing on page78 shows the proper weld preparation. If the metal thickness is equal to or less than ⅛ inch, no bevel preparation is needed. With respect to bubble-gum welds, all of us who are not professional welders will do it from time to time. When that happens, grind the mess away and be sure to get down to clean metal and re-weld.

Wire Feed Welding

The small wire feed welder is, hands down, the easiest welding machine to use for the novice. This machine delivers the filler wire, the inert gas and the arc simultaneously to the weld zone. This welder is also known as the MIG welder. The initials stand for Metallic Inert Gas welding. The Cee-Oh-two gas floods the weld zone while the puddle is being formed, thus preventing oxidization. In addition, rather thin metals may be successfully welded without blowing holes in them since the heat may be set low and the wire fed is of a small diameter.

Wire diameter range from .020 inch diameter up to .032 inch diameter for the small home workshop models. Some of these small welders are available in 120 VAC so they may be plugged into standard residential power. Most of these 120 volt units are of limited use. Lincoln makes a 120 volt system which works pretty good. Another variation on the 120 volt wire feed unit is one which uses no gas but instead a wire with a flux core. Obviously this flux core wire is very expensive compared with standard wire. At last check it was about 5 times more money per pound than ordinary wire-feed welding wire. It does have the convenience of not having to worry about inert gas and fool around with a tank and hose.

Wire comes in spools of 2 pound and 33 pound size on spools of 5 inch diameter and 12 inch diameter respectively. My experience with the small wire and small spool has not been too good. The small wire is very susceptible to *haystacking*, which means it collapses on itself inside the welder just before the feed rolls. In addition, the small diameters are subject to the same thing. Since switching to the 33 lb. roll and .030 wire, *haystacking* has been eliminated.

Wire feed tips are cheap and a quantity should be kept on hand. They are about 1/4 inch in diameter and about 1 inch long. The hole through them has just enough clearance so the wire you are using will pass through smoothly but also maintain electrical conductance with the wire. Before welding the wire should be clipped about ½ inch from the tip. The dimension is also known as *stick-out*. Many welding manual make a big deal over stick-out, but it is not that critical.

Before welding several tests should be run on your machine to determine the proper speed of the wire feed and the proper heat setting for the material you are welding. Obviously, the thicker the material the higher the heat setting. If the wire feed is too fast, the wire will push the hand unit away from the weld zone and if the wire feed is too slow, you will experience a *burn-back*, which is when the wire melts back into the tip, rendering the tip useless, hence, the need for several tips kept in reserve. The object is to set the wire speed to fuse at about ½ inch from the tip, maintaining a constant *stick-out* value.

One of the biggest advantages to the wire-feed welder is the ability to weld thin material by retarding the heat. Also, if and when holes are blown through material by welding, the wire feed machine can fill these holes by intermittent triggering and cooling cycles around the hole. In reminiscing about thin material welding, I remember watching a material and process research engineer butt weld a pair of .001 thick sheets of stainless steel. In this case he used a TIG system which is a Tungsten tip with inert gas. More often, this form of welding is done with an electron beam in a vacuum chamber.

Finally, one technique for welding thin sheets is a process known as *burn-down-flange*. The process involves bending a small flange on the edge of each piece of material about a 1/4 inch high. Then the small flanges are butted together and the flanges are burned down and fused together.

In summary, when I have to weld anything greater in thickness than 3/16, arc welding seems to be the best approach. Less than that thickness, the wire feed machine is most convenient. If you had your choice of only one machine, I would choose a wire feed unit. It is common to use multiple passes when welding thick pieces .

We did not discuss aluminum welding since it requires more sophisticated equipment, i.e., the heliarc welder. This is a machine which uses helium as the inert gas to shield the weld zone with a tungsten tip to create the arc. Filler aluminum is required along with considerable skill. I may be showing my ineptness, but when I need aluminum welded, I employ a professional.

We have only touched on the intricacies of welding . For more information in depth, the American Welding Society is one source. At your welding supply store books are available describing in detail each form of welding.

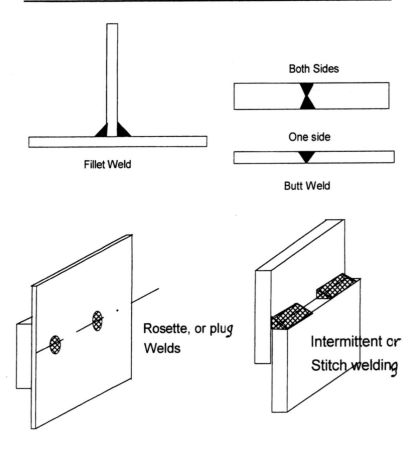

Fillet Weld

Both Sides

One side

Butt Weld

Rosette, or plug Welds

Intermittent or Stitch welding

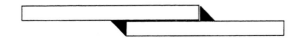

Lap Weld

Notes

Adhesive Bonding

The term adhesive bonding sound sort of redundant. But it should be pointed out that there are several forms of bonding, such as welding, and pressure bonding. What is pressure bonding? It is a form of metal. bonding where, after a period of time and pressure, the surface molecules of the two metals exchange atoms to interlock to weld themselves together without heat. Not only should the pressure be quite great but the action must take place in a vacuum, or to the exclusion of air such as in space. Also, a great deal of time is needed under these conditions. Hence, we do not consider this form of bonding for our buses in the near future.

Over 40 years ago, we began to glue airplane parts together. The common thermosetting resin such as epoxies and polyesters had been developed for practical applications.

At that time, we had pressurized clean rooms where white gloves must be worn for assembling these parts. The rooms were lightly pressurized so no' dust would wander in and settle on the parts. The white gloves were worn to protect the parts from the oil on our hands. The parts were encased in a blanket and a vacuum was drawn and they were cooked and cured in an autoclave. Even then, we would occasionally experience a bond failure .

Can you imagine a backyard conversion specialist going to all that trouble to glue some parts together? Obviously not! Today, however, we have had incredible advances in materials and technology. The techniques have become very *user friendly*, to borrow a computer term.

Adhesives for bonding a wide range of materials are now available, both in liquid form and tape form.

Surface Energies

Adhesion is the molecular attraction between unlike materials, similar to magnetic force. Strength of attraction is determined by the surface energy of the material. The higher the surface energy. the greater the attraction. The lower the surface energy, the weaker the attractive forces. On a high surface energy material the adhesive can flow or "wet out" to assure a stronger bond.

On an automobile unwaxed for years. water spreads on the surface in large puddles. This is high surface energy allowing the water to flow. In comparison, on a freshly waxed car, the water will bead up. This is low surface energy. the liquid (or adhesive) does not flow out.

Substrates

You must consider surface roughness or smoothness, coated or uncoated. flexibility. and part size. Double coated foam tapes can achieve more surface contact than thin tapes on rougher surfaces. If the surface is coated, the coating's surface energy must be considered. Smaller, more flexible parts can be bonded with thinner products such as adhesive transfer tapes. Larger, more rigid parts require thicker products such as double coated foam tapes.

Environmental Conditions

The types of exposure that your bonds will be required to resist must be taken into consideration. These include temperature extremes, sunlight (UV). water, oils or solvents. These environmental conditions will direct your adhesive choice.

Performance Requirements

You must consider what forms of stresses will be present: tensile, shear. cleavage or peel.

- **Tensile:** Forces perpendicular to the bond plane. Stress is distributed over the entire bond area. All the adhesive contributes to the bond strength.
- **Shear**: Forces parallel to the joint plane. As with tensile, stress is distributed over the entire bond area.
- **Cleavage**: Forces concentrated at the edge of the bond. Not all of the bond area is contributing to the overall strength at one time.
- **Peel**: Forces confined to the edge of the bond. At least one surface is flexible. Even less adhesive contributes to the bond strength that in cleavage.

Appearance

One of the big benefits of a tape joining system is that the tape is usually out of sight between bonded surfaces. In some instances, however, tape color or transparency will beimportant. For example, transparent 3M VHB ` 4910 Tape is virtually invisible when used to join clear plastic parts.

3M VHB
Double coated acrylic foam tape

High strength 3M VHB tapes are used throughout industry to replace mechanical fastening for permanent assemblies in many applications. The VHB material comes in two forms: transfer tape and double coated acrylic foam tape.

Transfer tape is a thin dry strip of permanent pressure sensitive adhesive transferred from the liner to the surface to be bonded. Ready to use. The foam tape provides higher strength, easier handling, cushioning, dampening and impact resistance. The foam tapes bond a wider range of materials. The more conformable foam helps improve void filling and flexibility, plus it has a broader range of temperature applications.

VHB tapes have been used to bond stainless steel scuff strips to aluminum wing flaps despite extreme ground to air temperature swings of 150°F to minus 40°F. This is an incredible compensation for differences in thermal expansion. This product has been used in truck bodies eliminating rivets reducing fatigue cracks and corrosion while saving labor time and cost. One truck body manufacturer has raised its's truck cab warranty from 100,000 miles to 300,000.

VHB tape can glue wood to glass for decorative purposes. A common use is to bond muntin bars to thermopane windows to create a colonial effect. The bond resists weathering and UV light. The tape will glue metal painted surfaces to each other.

In May of this year (1997), we had the experience to use this material on a bus conversion. The owner wanted to have his roof raised which was accomplished. It was then ready to have the new siding installed between the windows. First we selected 18 gauge steel so there would be no uneven thermal expansion. The panels we pre-sheared at the suppliers so all we had to do was stick the skin to the bus. First the framework of the bus was painted with etching primer. Then the pre-sheared cold rolled steel panels were primed on both sides with the same etching primer. We use an adhesive tape designated VHB 4950 one inch wide. Although one and one-half inch would have been preferred, this size was adequate for the strength and was all that was locally available.

Prior to the tape application all the taped area surfaces were cleaned with common rubbing isopropyl alcohol. The tape was applied to the framework of the bus: the sills, the headers and the vertical members. At the end of each piece of tape a section of the release tape was folded back. Two guys held the skin on the outside and positioned it. After it was carefully positioned, the man on the inside began to strip the release tape away as one of the outside men patted the material to the frame. Then the inside man stripped away all the protective paper and the outside guys patted the material down. The next step was to use a pressure roller against the outside material at each frame position. And, wah-lah!, the siding was done. No drilling, no busted drills, no mis-pulled rivets, no cussin'. Nothing to do but stand back, admire and pop a beer.

The VHB tape develops about 20 percent of it's strength right away. Twenty-four hours later it is up to about 90 percent, with 100 percent being achieved after 72 hours dwell time. This may be accelerated with heat and pressure.

The dynamic shear at room temperature is rated at 80 psi. It's tensile strength is 140 psi and it's 90 degree peel adhesion is 20 lbs. per inch. It has a short term temperature tolerance of 300 °F and a long term tolerance of 200 °F. Although most liquid adhesives shown a much higher shear strength, this material is quite adequate for applying siding to a bus. Especially under condition where the siding is not structural such as the siding between the windows of an Eagle bus.

As a *rule of thumb*, 3M suggests 4square inches of tape per pound of siding. Let us assume you wish to cover an area 24" x 30" with 18 gauge steel. The steel will weight .045 x 24 x 30 x .3 = 9.72 lbs. Lets simplify by declaring the steel weights 10 lbs. Therefore, 10 x 4

= 40 square inches of tape. If we used tape 1 inch wide, we need only 40 inches. If we lay the tape all around the panel, we have 2 x 22 + 2 x 30 = 104 square inches of tape. This gives us a safety factor of over 2.5. Based on the shear strength, we have a capacity to react 8,320 lbs.

For further information, contact 3M Industrial Tape and Specialties Division at 1(800)362-3550.

Sikaflex
Elastic Bonding Systems

Sikaflex is a urethane based elastomer and is used for both sealing and bonding. Manufacturers of transportation equipment have traditionally used a wide range of mechanical fasteners in the construction of their products. Rivets, welds, bolts and screws are commonly used throughout the industry. Past attempts at bonding in this industry have failed because the adhesives were complicated to mix, difficult to apply and too brittle when cured. The revolutionary new Elastic Bonding Systems from Sika now make bonding possible. These systems require no mixing, are easy to apply and maintain their elastic properties even after full cure. This offers many advantages to the user:

1. Even Stress Distribution Sika elastic adhesives distribute stress over the entire bond line for a stronger, longer lasting joint.

2. Absorb Thermal Expansion. Different materials often exhibit different coefficients of expansion. The use of an elastic adhesive safeguards the load bearing joint

and reduces stress.

3. Increase Torsional Stress. This adds strength and may allow the use of lighter materials.

4. Seal and Bond. Elastic adhesives systems seal as well as bond. Most rigid fasteners need to be sealed, why not bond and seal in one step?

The following list of items are currently being bonded and seals in buses, trains and Rvs.: Lap Joints, Vents, Body Seams, Sidewalls, Sunroof, Roof to Frame, Luggage floor, Passenger floor, Fiberglass caps, Glass to Frame, Interior Fixtures, and Emblems and Trim.

Sika Products

Sikaflex 201 - The original Sika Elastic Sealant. This product is smooth, easy to gun and adheres to most substrates. Ideal for all sealing applications.

Sikaflex 221 - This versatile product is the most popular adhesive/sealant in the transportation industry. It is an excellent sealer and can handle many light bonding applications

Sikaflex 252 - A high viscous, high strength adhesive, this remarkable product can replace rivets, screws, welds and other mechanical fasteners. Seals and bonds in one step.

Sikaflex 255FC - A high viscous, high strength adhesive, this product is designed specifically for excellent adhesion to glass and metal. Ideal for windshields, side windows, sunroofs, etc.

SikaTack Ultrafast - This revolutionary product uses heat instead of moisture to "precure" the adhesive. The product is heated before application using a SikaTack oven for extremely fast strength build up. Specifically designed for fast installation of glass to metal.

Sikaflex 360HC - This is the fastest curing, one component adhesive system available. The "hot-cure" product is cold applied to the substrate to be bonded. Then the entire assembly is exposed to heat or energy (induction, UV, microwave, etc.). This heat catalyzes the cure. Full cure can be reached in a matter of minutes.

The last two items, Sikatack and Sikaflex 360HC require a heat cure and do not lend themselves to our backyard conversion specialists normal facilities. And, Sikaflex 255FC has an unusually high shear strength (550 psi) and an associated viscosity. This causes it to be somewhat difficult to apply without a power applicator.

For pure bonding strength and ease of application, my choice is Sikaflex 252. It has a shear strength of 350 psi and a tensile strength of about 500 psi. It comes in black or white in a 10.5 ounce cartridge. It's consumption rate is about 24 feet with a ¼ inch diameter round bead. It may be applied in temperatures from 60°F to 110°F., and is tack free in less than an hour. It is an atmospheric-moisture cure system.

Sikaflex 221 comes in black, white, gray and tan, and in cartridges, pails and drums. It's shear strength is is a respectable 165 psi, which is twice the value of the 3M tape discussed earlier. It's tensile strength is approximately 250 psi..

Now, let's assume you want to apply a one-piece side panel to your bus frame between your windows. It is easily seen that the part can be clamped at each end using "C" clamps and an angle iron to apply even pressure. How do you apply clamping pressure in the middle where the intermediate frames are? I've given this problem considerable thought. One way to do it would be to park your bus against a solid concrete building and use jacks to apply pressure or wedge sticks against stiff pieces of wood. Another way would be to secure a frame along the bottom and pull tension on it from the other side. I think the simplest way might be to screw a light angle or stiffener to the outside at each frame position and use it to apply even pressure along the frame. This technique will, however, leave small blemishes where the screws penetrated the siding. This can be easily taken care of with small applications of local body putty.

For further information contact Sika Corporation at 22211 Telegraph Road, Southfield, MI 48034, (313)354-6555.

Goop

GOOP is a product of Eclectic Products, 1(800)767-4667. It is a flexible adhesive with considerable more adhesion than silicone and a very high shear and peel strength. It is attacked by many solvents such as gasoline, Toluene, Perchloroethylene and the like. However, it is quite resistant to water, acids and bases including wine, salt, fertilizers, milk and hydraulic oils to name a few.

E-6000 is the most common Goop. Almost any dry substrate may be bonded to any other. Some examples are glass to metal to plastic to wood to tile to fiberglass to concrete to rubber to fabric to brick to leather and on and on. It's uses are really quite amazing.

This~multi-purpose, one component, self leveling adhesive and sealant is so versatile that it practically eliminates the need for any other glue, epoxy silicone, rubber cement or patch kit. First and foremost, E-6000 is possibly the strongest toughest adhesive and sealant available for industrial applications. Though E-6000 has a very high tensile strength, it also remains extremely flexible, even when used underwater. This elasticity makes E-6000 ideal when used as an adhesive of sealant between surfaces with dissimilar expansion coefficients

While strength is important, versatility is E-6000's most unique feature. Quite possibly, it is the only adhesive and sealant known to man that will bond to all these different porous and non-porous substrates: metal, wood, plastic, tile, glass, fiberglass, concrete, brick, rubber, canvas, leather, vinyl and fabric. Furthermore, E-6000 can be applied to both oil and water based paints, or it can be painted over by both of these. And finally, E-6000 is extremely non-corrosive, and except for a few high-powered solvents, may be used in contact with most chemical solutions.

Because E-6000 has so many different uses, it is also made in four convenient colors: clear, black, white and gray. And, if that isn't enough variety for you, it is also supplied in 6 convenient sizes: 3.7 fl. oz. tubes, 10.2 fl. oz. cartridges, 1 qt. cans, 1 gal. cans, 5gal, pails or 55 gal. drums.

Contact Adhesives

Contact adhesives are used to bond headliners, plastics laminates (such as Formica), carpet and wall panels, to name a few.

Plastic laminate bonding uses a solvent based, and more recently, a water-based contact adhesive. The plan is to apply the adhesive and let them skin over then bring the parts into contact and pressure roll them. Headline adhesives are also known as Landau roof adhesives and are available from automotive upholstery supply companies. Such characteristics as peel, shear and tensile strengths are of secondary importance with these form of adhesive. One word of caution is when laminating plastic laminates, do not use lacquer thinner as a solvent since lacquer thinner contains a small amount of oil and will cause a failure in the bond

Power Glue
(also known as Crazy Glue)
and more properly called *cyanoacrylates*

Cyanoacrylates (CA's) have become the adhesive of choice for most hobby and household applications. High quality CA's such as INSTA-CURE, when used properly, form bonds that in many cases are stronger than the material that is being adhered. INSTA-CURE is a highly refined CA which, combined with its freshness, gives a guaranteed 2 year shelf life.

CA's are reactive monomers that chemically link (polymerize) when pressed into a thin film. The very thin layer of water moisture present on most surfaces acts as an alkali, or weak base, which is the catalyst that results in bonding; however, the presence of detectable amounts of water usually degrades the performance of CA's.

INSTA-CURE has a water-thin viscosity that wicks deep into joints by capillary action and cures in a matter of a few seconds. Surfaces to be bonded must be tight fitting and should be held together while you apply the CA around the edges of the seam. At the moment CA's cure, they give off a vapor that can irritate the nose and eyes, so be prepared. Thin CA's work very well on balsa since they penetrate into the wood and form more than just a surface bond.

INSTA-CURE is a higher viscosity CA for loose fitting joints in which the adhesive must bridge gaps. Normally, the thicker CA is applied to one surface and then the parts are held tightly together for about 5 to 15 seconds. For large surface areas, including those with close fitting joints such as laminations, INSTA-CURE+ should also be used. To prevent premature curing, don't spread the glue into a thin film. Lay down a serpentine bead with about 1" separations on one surface, then assemble the parts, letting the pressure spread the CA out.

INSTA-SET is a catalyst which acts as an accelerator that allows CA's to quickly cure in thick layers by enhancing the alkaline conditions during polymerization. INSTA-SET in a spray bottle is normally used to cure the CA that flows from joints when parts are pressed together. Applying an additional bead of thick CA along a seam and then curing it with INSTA-SET significantly enhances a joint's strength. For difficult to bond materials, INSTA-SET is formulated with a strawberry scent and activates CA in 6 to 8 seconds without any degrading of the CA's strength, which can occur with many other accelerators. It is compatible with all surfaces, even clear plastic and white foam.

MAXI-CURE extra thick CA is the best CA for most plastics, including GE's Lexan. MAXI-CURE is the best choice for plastic model assembly. When used with INSTA-SET, it works better than any putty for modifying of filling voids. It can be carved with a knife or razor blade and sanded and feathered to form a finish indistinguishable from plastic.

MAXI-CURE bonds fiberglass, hardwood, metal and rubber better than any other hobby adhesive. For gluing to the inside, cloth textured surface of fiberglass, scrape the area to be bonded with a razor blade or coarse sandpaper before using MAXI-CURE or any other adhesive. It also is best for bonding the tires for R/C cars.

SUPER-GOLD and SUPER-GOLD+ are our odorless INSTA-CURE CA's they are non-frosting and take only 2 to 3 seconds longer to bond. There are no fumes that irritate the nose and eyes. The SUPER-GOLD's do not attack white foam; therefore, they can be used in the building of foam core wings and the assembly and repair of plastic and foam ARF's. They will not fog clear plastic. SUPER-GOLD+ is ideal for attaching clear canopies in plastic model kits; owever,MAXI-CURE is still recommended for assembling the rest of plastic kits. Wood can be bonded to white foam with SUPER-GOLD+ in less than fifteen seconds. For bonding foam to foam, spray a very light fog of INSTA-SET to one piece and apply SUPER-GOLD+ to the other before joining. Excess INSTA-Set may create too much heat, which can melt the foam. Both SUPER-GOLD's cure to a more flexible consistency for better shock absorption. Whenever a large amount of CA is to be used in such applications as saturating fiberglass or Kevlar, SUPER-GOLD eliminates the irritating fumes from the evaporating monomer that make repeated use of CA unpleasant at times.

UN-CURE debonder will soften cured CA. If parts are bonded incorrectly or your fingers are stuck together, a few drops of   UN-CURE will dissolve the CA in about a minute. Apply on bonded skin and roll apart fingers. Once unstuck, use acetone to clean off softened CA, then wash off with soap and water.

With all CA's, the closer the parts fit together, the stronger the bond. Always hold the bonding surfaces as tightly as possible. Any rough spots on the mating surfaces should be smoothed out. Although CA's will hold objects together with considerable strength within seconds, the full strength of the bond is not reached for several hours. Allow for this before subjecting parts to maximum stress. Also, CA's are generally a little less brittle and have higher strength when they are allowed to cure on their own.

Heat and moisture will decrease the shelf life of CA's. Unopened bottles can be stored in a freezer or refrigerator, but allow them to reach room temperature before using. Keep your bottles in a cool place that won't be exposed to direct sunlight and store away from bottles of accelerators. Due to the freshness of most CA's, their shelf life is guaranteed for 24 months.

For the initial opening of the top, loosen top first to relieve internal pressure, then hold the bottle against a near vertical surface and cut off the top 1/32" with a knife or razor blade without squeezing the bottle. To prevent clogging, do not let the tip of the nozzle touch a surface that has been sprayed with INSTA-SET. Before replacing the colored cap, sit the bottle down hard to knock the remaining CA back into the bottle before squeezing it in an upright position to blow air through the nozzle, then wipe the tip clean.

Our CA's come in 1/2 oz., 1 oz. and 2 oz. sizes, along with an 8 oz. that has a no mess, easy pour bottle for economical refilling of our regular bottles. In addition to our line of extended tips and fine Teflon tubing that allows very small, controlled amounts of CA to be applied, we have CA applicators that come in both a regular and fine tip. They are like a disposable eye-dropper that greatly resists clogging. Just squeeze the bulb and insert into an open CA bottle to draw out the amount you need. When using the Teflon tubing, cut one end at a 45 degree angle before inserting no more than 1/4" into the bottle top.

Epoxies

If CA's are the cure-all for just about all bonding problems, you may be wondering, "Why do I need epoxy?" One primary reason is price. Epoxy costs are about one fourth that of CA. When large objects are being bonded, economics can be a deciding factor on choice of adhesive. The specific characteristics of epoxies also give them advantages in some applications.

All epoxies are mixed with a 50-50 ratio. Any scrap material or paper scratch pad can be used as a mixing surface. We have found, however, that the plastic tops to coffee cans work best due to their flexibility, which allows the unused cured epoxy to be released and thrown away. Squeeze out equal length beads of the desired amount of epoxy, then mix together thoroughly with a popsicle stick or scrap piece of material.

In cold weather, epoxy takes longer to cure (too cold and usually they never fully cure)) and becomes more difficult to get out of the bottle, especially if it's less than 1/2 full. The epoxies can be heated in a microwave oven for about 10 seconds so that they flow easier. The heating process, with the caps off, also releases any moisture that can be absorbed by epoxies. Their shelf life, therefore, is virtually unlimited.

Acetone works as the best solvent for cleaning epoxy from brushes and unwanted surfaces before it cures. If epoxy gets on surfaces that acetone will attack, use isopropyl alcohol. We do not recommend any additives for thinning epoxies due to their effect on curing and overall strength. If thin epoxy is required, either use heat or switch to EX-SLOW or FINISH-CURE.

Epoxies bond best to clean, textured surfaces. Smooth, non-porous surfaces should be roughened with coarse sandpaper to improve adhesion. A small amount of CA can be used in strategic locations to hold parts in place while the epoxies cure. The minute designations for epoxies begin to set up after being mixed in a large mass. When spread into thinner layers, the working time in increased significantly (except QUIK-CURE). Working time decreases approximately 25 percent at temperatures above 90 degrees F.

Don't panic if your skin comes in contact with either epoxy or CA. While contact should be avoided, uncured epoxy can be washed from your skin with soap and water. Allergic reactions are rare. Cured epoxy and CA can be peeled off the skin and usually are gone after a full day of normal activity. UN-CURE will debond any body parts that get stuck together if a peeling action (never pulling) doesn't part them.

Woodworking Glues

The earliest material used to bond wood goes back several thousand years, the earliest glues being made from such materials as mud and animal excrement. Progress over the centuries brought the use of animal glues from hoof, horn and bone extracts as well as vegetable glues based on flour.

The type of glues that were used were confined to what materials there were available then. Fishing communities developed glues from fish bones and fish meal, while farming communities used flour made not only from wheat and other grains, but also casein, blood albumen and other animal products. Natural resins such as rosin, manilla gum and shellac were dissolved in alcohol for use as adhesives and to make lacquers for surface decoration and protection. These simple products continued to be in use until the end of the last century, when the first synthetic resins were developed.

The most important discovery was made by Leo Baekeland who can be regarded as the founding father of modern plastics and synthetic resin technology. One of his many discoveries was that certain substances can be reacted with formaldehyde to produce sticky resinous materials, the first being a phenol-formaldehyde which was named Bakelite. One version of this resin which could be dissolved in alcohol and used as an adhesive in the same way as shellac was called "novolac". Variants made from same raw materials but through a slightly different method were insoluble in alcohol and required heat to harden them.

This made them more or less unsuitable for joining wood as unduly high temperatures were required with these early products. In fact, in the early days, neither novolacs nor resoles could be regarded as ideal adhesives, and animal glues continued to be used until the 1930s when urea formaldehyde resins were introduced. Since the introduction of urea and melamine resins, the chemical industry has developed a vast range of woodworking adhesives for every conceivable application.

Resin classification The resins used in woodworking can be classified into two main groups; thermo-setting resins are converted by heat to a tough infusible mass; and thermo-plastic resins (or hot-melts) are applied hot and form a bond on cooling.

A third group of adhesives consists of solutions of natural or synthetic rubbers which form a bond by the evaporation of solvent. Commonly known as contact adhesives, they are rarely used in woodworking but find widespread use in upholstery work.

Thermo-setting resins

Thermo-setting resins harden by a chemical reaction which causes the molecules to form a three-dimensional structure to produce a solid mass and at the same time, bond to the wood. These resins can be grouped into four classes: adhesives made by reacting formaldehyde with urea, melamine, phenol and other materials; adhesives made by reacting tannin with phenol or formaldehyde; isocyanate resins; epoxy resins.

Urea formaldehyde glues

These were the first synthetic resins to be widely adopted, and although they appeared some 60 years ago, they are still the most widely used adhesives in the woodworking industry.

They are made by reacting formaldehyde with urea: the raw materials are heated in an alkaline solution to first produce methyl urea, which is not an adhesive. As the reaction continues, this time in an acid condition after neutralising the alkali, the elimination of water produces reactive groups which link to bridge the molecules.

The reaction is stopped by neutralising the acid and evaporating the remaining water to give either a high solids syrup or powder. Taken to the limit, this reaction yields a solid mass, so if the process is not properly controlled, the resin will set in the reaction vessel, requiring the removal of several tons of hardened gel!

To produce a resin powder, the syrup is sprayed through small holes into a heated chamber through a jet of hot air at 200°C.

Urea formaldehyde glues are sold either as a one-pack powder, or as two-pack products consisting of the resin powder or syrup, to which a hardener such as ammonium chloride is added. In the former case, the hardener is added to the powdered resin and further additions may be made of extenders and fillers such as wheat flour, rye flour, pea or bean flour, or mineral fillers such as kaolin or calcium sulphate. The glue is prepared by mixing the powder with water, adding the hardener and then applying it to the surface to be joined. The acid hardener initiates the completion of the cross-linking reaction that was stopped during the final stage of manufacture. Heating the glue line accelerates hardening.

Hardeners used with urea formaldehyde resins are always very weak. Strong acids may attack the wood or hydrolyse the joint and lead to glue line failure. With the need to reduce the emission of formaldehyde from wood products, the formaldehyde:urea ratio has been reduced from about 1.8:1 or 2.0:1 to below 1.6:1, or in some cases to as low as 1.2:1. Not only does this lengthen the time for manufacture, but glues with a low content of free formaldehyde require longer hardening times. They also tend to impart a lower bond strength, lower resistance to moisture and reduced stability in storage. The performance of urea formaldehyde glues can be enhanced by additives such as melamine, tannin, sodium disulphite and some mild organic acids. However, their performance on exposure to water and elevated temperatures is poor and they are not ideal for use where joints may be exposed to hot, humid atmospheres or to inclement weather.

Urea formaldehyde resins find a wide range of applications in the manufacture of particleboard, hardboard, MDF, blockboard. They are the most popular glues for veneering and for assembly work for both furniture and joinery, although more water resistant glues are now preferred for joinery that will be exposed to wet or humid conditions.

Melamine formaldehyde resins

Melamine formaldehyde glues were introduced some 20 years after urea formaldehyde resins which they resemble in many ways. Both are made by reacting the amino part with the formaldehyde under similar conditions of heating in solution, although the formaldehyde reacts more readily with the melamine than does urea. It is thus easier to make low formaldehyde emission melamine formaldehyde than comparable urea formaldehyde glues. Both are used with similar hardeners, and the same fillers and extenders can be added. Both are clear, water-white in colour, which makes the glue line more or less inconspicuous.

MF glues need higher temperatures than UF glues, but they show better resistance to water and high temperatures. The inevitable disadvantage is cost. MF resin may be up to four or five times the cost of UF glues, but this can sometimes be reduced by blending UF glues with MF resins to give what are now called MUF glues, whose properties vary in relation to the resin blend. For example, a 40:60 blend of melamine and urea resins will give a marked improvement in the resistance to accelerated aging. Melamine glues are used for making special grades of chipboard and especially the weather and moisture resistant grades of MDF. They are also used for joinery that must withstand moist or wet conditions.

Phenol formaldehyde resins

Although phenolic resins were available before UF and MF types, they were not used in woodworking until the 1930s, and now find their main uses in the manufacture of marine plywood, chipboard and OSB for the construction industry. Resoles, the only types used for board production, are made by reacting with formaldehyde in an alkaline solution. They need high curing temperatures, but produce a glue line with outstanding resistance to water, heat and contaminants.

Novolacs are made in an acid solution with much lower proportions of formaldehyde to phenol than resoles. Hexamethylene tetramine is added when novolacs are used for hot gluing, their only uses in the woodworking industry being in the production of special grades of wafer board which are made with novolac powder, and in the production of densified wood.

Densified wood is made by laying up veneer in the same way as plywood, but instead of applying the adhesive to form a glue line between the layers of veneer, the veneer itself is first impregnated with resin solution. It is then allowed to drain, laid up to give the desired thickness and finally compressed under very high pressure which reduces the thickness and produces a heavy, dense laminate with excellent wear properties.

Phenol-resorcinol resins

Phenol-resorcinol resins are made by adding resorcinol to a resole during the final stages of manufacture. These dark brown adhesives are used for the manufacture of laminated beams thanks to two properties: firstly, their resistance to water, and secondly, their high reactivity, which means they can be used for gluing at very low temperatures, sometimes down to 5°C. They are catalysed with paraformalde-hyde before use, and the joints may be cured at temperatures up to about 70°C. Wood flour is often added to improve the gap filling properties in view of the nature of the timber that is being bonded.

Tannin resins

Tannin, a natural phenol, occurs in wood in quite large quantities, especially in oak bark, and is reacted with phenol formaldehyde resin after impurities such as sugars and gums have been extracted. Their use is not widespread, but they are adopted in some countries for making chipboard and MDF with good resistance to moisture.

Isocyanate resins

Although they have been used as casting resins and paint media since about 1950, the woodworking industry showed little or no interest in them until 1975. They are now used in the manufacture of chipboard and MDF where high durability is demanded, forming a complex chemical bond with the lignin and cellulose in the wood to produce a bond of exceptional quality. It is very costly, but as the quantity used in chipboard manufacture is very low, they can prove economical. For example, due to the nature of the bond, about 15% less wood is used in chipboard to obtain the same mechanical strength.

Epoxy resins

Epoxies are made by reacting bisphenol-A with epichlorhydrin to yield a range of resins of different molecular weights and characteristics. Various materials can be employed as hardeners, but polyamides are now the most widely used. Epoxy resins will harden at room temperature with little need for the application of pressure to the joint. They have good filling properties - they are usually used in the woodworking industry as low molecular weight liquids with no addition of solvent, and as they harden by an addition reaction without the loss of any reaction products, there is little loss of volume on hardening.

Thermo-plastic adhesive: Polyvinyl acetate resin

This thermo-plastic polymer is usually employed in the form of an aqueous emulsion and although it may be cured to an apparently hard mass by heating, it can still be softened at high temperatures.

It can be modified to give a high or low viscosity, rigidity or flexibility, and dyes or pigments may be added to impart a colour. Two versions are used in the woodworking industry: the homopolymer which softens readily when heated, and the co-polymer which is used with a catalyst to give an improved bond with better resistance to water and heat. Maize or other starches can be added to increase the viscosity and prevent the glue from being squeezed out of the joint or through the pores in veneer. Mineral fillers can also be used, but care must be taken to avoid alkaline materials which can impede the hardening reaction.

The addition of metallic salts such as chromium or aluminium nitrate will improve the resistance to water, although the pot-life is reduced. Additions of UF, MF and isocyanate resins are sometimes made to improve the properties of the adhesive. PVA glues are widely used for veneering, bonding paper and PVC foils to chipboard, hardboard and for cabinet assembly work.

Hot-melt systems: Eva hot-melts

Ethylene vinyl acetate adhesives are a blend of EVA resin-which provides the bulk and is the main contributor to the adhesion-a resin to impart `tack' and a mineral filler to reinforce the cohesion and filling qualities of the glue and reduce the cost. In addition, there may be small amounts of wax to control the open time and rate of setting, and an anti-oxidant to minimize the tendency to oxidize in the hot glue pot.

Manufacture begins with loading the resin, filler, and anti-oxidant into a heated Z-blade mixer, a massive machine which pounds and cuts the hot resin and ensures complete blending. Once a consistent mix is obtained, the remaining ingredients are added and the mixer is run for a further 30 minutes, after which the mix is turned out onto a chill table where it is allowed to set before being cut into granules or extruded to form granules of the desired shape and size.

The shape can be very important in ensuring quick heating without oxidation in the glue pot of the edge-bander. The granules are coated with talc to prevent blocking in the package. Extruders are also used for mixing, and have the advantage of producing the adhesive in a continuous flow so that it can be more easily formed into granules. However, extruders do not always achieve such intimate mixing as a Z-blade mixer and it is often better to start the mixing in a Z-blade or a blender.

The basic EVA polymer may have a low, medium

or high content of vinyl acetate, a higher acetate content imparting the following: adhesion, compatibility with fillers,
longer open time, lower heat resistance, and greater solubility in solvents EVA hot-melts predominate in the edgebanding sector, occupying about 80% of the market. They are also used for some assembly work, especially in the twin glue system in conjunction with PVA glues. In this process, the hot-melt is used to hold the joint while the PVA sets and ultimately provides the main bond.

Polyamide resins

Polyamides are used in small quantities, mainly for bonding edgebandings where high resistance to elevated temperatures is needed. They are similar to nylon and are made by reacting conventional fatty acid polymers (similar to alkyds) with diamine. They are difficult to use as their melting point is very high and there is a risk of oxidation which can seriously impair the adhesive properties. For this reason, they are sometimes used in nitrogen blanketed glue dispensers. Polyamides are used in the US for edgebanding, but are not widely favoured elsewhere as they are several times more costly than EVA and polyurethanes.

Polyolefines

These are not widely used in the woodworking industry as their adhesive properties are not outstanding; but for edgebanding, they offer a compromise in terms of heat resistance between EVA and polyamides, at a more acceptable cost. They are based on blends of polypropylene, polyethylene and similar resins with isobutyl-isoprene rubbers to impart tack. They have better melting characteristics than polyamides, good bond strength and a narrow melting range which ensures quick setting. On the other hand, the adhesive properties are poor when using smooth surfaced materials such as PVC.

Polyurethane resins

The polyurethane hot-melt resins used for edgebanding behave like conventional hot-melt products during application, but subsequently react with the moisture in the air and the materials which they have bonded to produce a glue line with properties similar to those from a thermo-setting resin. They are made by reacting a diole with a diisocyanate to produce a cross-linked structure with highly reactive groups which account for the subsequent reaction with hydroxyls.

They are used at temperatures lower than those for EVA resins, usually about 100-140°C. However, they must be protected from moisture in storage and during use, which requires the use of nitrogen blanketed equipment. They are particularly useful where a high performance bond is needed, for example when bonding lippings onto fire doors. They are about six times more costly than EVA, but this can be justified when the highest performance is essential.

In one edgebander capable of using polyurethanes without nitrogen blanketing, the cartridge glue dispenser melts only the surface of the adhesive block at the moment of spreading. Once the panel has been glued, the front of the dispenser is sealed by a sliding plate which protects the glue from any contact with air or moisture.

Silicone

Silicone is an excellent material to use for sealing any gaps or adhering surfaces together. Silicone is a very flexible material that can withstand significant joint movement without cracking or pulling away. Silicones' products, ·when used properly, will not yellow, shrink or crack like many latex products.

The following are guidelines for preparing various materials:

Concrete, Masonry & Stone : Use a wire brush to remove all old sealant and dirt, dust and loose particles. All contaminants and impurities must be cleaned off, such as, concrete form release agents, water repellents and other surface treatments and protective coatings.

Porous Surfaces: Use sandpaper or wire brush where necessary to provide a sound, clean surface.

Metal, Glass & Plastic: These surfaces should be cleaned with a solvent such as mineral spirits or lacquer thinner.

Note: Do not use GE silicone sealant products on any galvanized surface. Cleaning with detergent or soap and water is NOT recommended. When using solvents, always wipe the surface dry with a clean cloth or lintless paper towels. Never allow solvent to air dry or evaporate without wiping. NOTE: Do not use soap to clean surfaces to be sealed because silicone will not adhere to surfaces covered with any soap scum

.   An application not hardening (not curing) is typically due to aged product, so that the chemical that makes the silicone harden is no longer active. Silicone should cure within 24 hours. If it has been over 24 hours, you should determine when the silicone was purchased. If purchased within one year, find the following information on the tube: stock number, batch code or a description of type of silicone and call the manufacturer.

Silicone sealants can be tested before using to ensure proper curing by placing small amount on a piece of cardboard and watching for a skin to form on the surface of the silicone. If no skin has formed after 15 minutes, the silicone is probably too old and will not cure.

If silicone has not cured, it has to be completely removed from the affected surfaces before any new material can be applied. To remove, scrape off the majority of the "bead" then use a solvent such as 100% mineral spirits or lacquer thinner to thoroughly wash. Use caution while using these solvents. They will dissolve paints and other finishing materials.

A 3/16" bead "normally" cures in 24 hours. We say normally because humidity affects the curing process and different parts of the country experience varying degrees of humidity. Lack of humidity will retard this process. If the product shows some sign of curing, such as a change in original consistency, it will cure. It just may be taking longer than normal. It may take up to 48 hours for sealant to cure under extreme conditions Silicone II products provide 6-8 minutes tooling time, 45-60 minutes before they are tack- free, and 24 hour cure time (1/8-1/4" thickness, 70 degrees). Standard Silicone products provide 2-5 minutes tooling time, 20-30 minutes before they are tack-free, and 24 hour cure time (1/8-1/4" thickness, 70 degrees). The silicone should start to skin within 15-20 minutes. If used in the bathroom, you should wait 12 hours before using the affected fixtures. Any type of pressure such as touching or pressing on the uncured sealants will cause indentations.

There is no data available for shelf life of sealant after it has been opened. Opened tubes of sealant should be stored in a cool, dry place. Before storing, a small amount of silicone should be purged out so fresh silicone will be at the top of tip. Replace the cap, or quickly wrap electrician's tape or duct tape around the tip or put a nail down the nozzle and wrap tape over it.

It is VERY difficult to remove silicone from a surface. However, if you must remove it, follow the suggestions below.

On Smooth, Non-porous Surfaces

To remove silicone sealant from surfaces, first remove as much as possible by cutting or scraping excess sealant from surface. For ceramic tile, marble, Formica, fiberglass, etc., use 100% mineral spirits (turpentine) and a non-abrasive scouring pad. Test solvent on a hidden area of the surface to ensure that discoloration will not occur. If discoloration does occur, contact the manufacturer of the surface for further assistance. For glass surfaces, use a razor blade to remove as much as possible, then apply mineral spirits. Remove excess with a towel or other suitable cleaning utensil that will not mar the surface, i.e., non abrasive pad. NOTE: For surfaces such as hard plastics or painted surfaces, including cars, use rubbing alcohol and a soft cloth. Do not use mineral spirits.

On Rough, Porous Surfaces

To remove silicone from a porous/rough surface, (concrete, brick, wallpaper) remove as much as possible (same as smooth surface). If necessary, use a wire brush in conjunction with mineral spirits. NOTE: We do not recommend use of a wire brush to remove sealant from wood surfaces, as so doing could damage the wood. Also, mineral spirits should not be used if the wood has any type of finish on it. Test solvent on a hidden area before applying generally

There is nothing that will dissolve silicone. If reapplying silicone to the area, remove the old sealant. Then clean the area with a disinfectant. If mold or mildew is present apply rubbing alcohol. Let dry before re-applying silicone.

Conclusions

This small book is as complete as I felt it should be. I did not included ways to keep your cupboards from flying open as you sweep quickly around curves, and I have received mild criticism from my beloved for that failure. I will appreciate any suggestions from other bus nuts for any omissions other than the one just mentioned. If this can't answer all your questions, it probably gave you enough information to know who and what to ask.

Good Luck!

Index

Order Blank

Name:_____

Address:_____

City_____ State ____ Zip_____

Phone (   ) _____

The Bus Converter's Bible ___ @ $39.95 _____

The Joys of Busing   ___ @ $19.95 _____

The Gospel of Gauges   ___ @ $9.95 _____

Classy Cabinets   ___ @ $19.95 _____

Fascinating Fastener Facts ___ @ $14.95 _____

       Shipping $5.00 Add $1 per book   _____

      California residents add 7.75%   _____

                Total Order   _____

Make checks payable to:
       Winlock Galey
      26135 Murrieta Road
      Sun City Ca, 92585

     Or call (909)943-0014
             or
  Book Network at (800)205-8254

We accept MasterCard, Visa, American Express

Card number _____

Expiration date_____ Signed: _____